GLENCOE
MATHEMATICS

Algebra 2

Chapter 12
Resource Masters

Glencoe
McGraw-Hill

New York, New York
Columbus, Ohio
Chicago, Illinois
Peoria, Illinois
Woodland Hills, California

Consumable Workbooks

Many of the worksheets contained in the Chapter Resource Masters booklets are available as consumable workbooks.

Study Guide and Intervention Workbook	0-07-828029-X
Skills Practice Workbook	0-07-828023-0
Practice Workbook	0-07-828024-9

ANSWERS FOR WORKBOOKS The answers for Chapter 12 of these workbooks can be found in the back of this Chapter Resource Masters booklet.

Glencoe/McGraw-Hill

A Division of The McGraw·Hill Companies

Send all inquiries to:
The McGraw-Hill Companies
8787 Orion Place
Columbus, OH 43240-4027

ISBN: 0-07-828015-X

Algebra 2
Chapter 12 Resource Masters

2 3 4 5 6 7 8 9 10   066   11 10 09 08 07 06 05 04 03

Contents

Vocabulary Builder vii

Lesson 12-1
Study Guide and Intervention 699–700
Skills Practice 701
Practice 702
Reading to Learn Mathematics 703
Enrichment 704

Lesson 12-2
Study Guide and Intervention 705–706
Skills Practice 707
Practice 708
Reading to Learn Mathematics 709
Enrichment 710

Lesson 12-3
Study Guide and Intervention 711–712
Skills Practice 713
Practice 714
Reading to Learn Mathematics 715
Enrichment 716

Lesson 12-4
Study Guide and Intervention 717–718
Skills Practice 719
Practice 720
Reading to Learn Mathematics 721
Enrichment 722

Lesson 12-5
Study Guide and Intervention 723–724
Skills Practice 725
Practice 726
Reading to Learn Mathematics 727
Enrichment 728

Lesson 12-6
Study Guide and Intervention 729–730
Skills Practice 731
Practice 732
Reading to Learn Mathematics 733
Enrichment 734

Lesson 12-7
Study Guide and Intervention 735–736
Skills Practice 737
Practice 738
Reading to Learn Mathematics 739
Enrichment 740

Lesson 12-8
Study Guide and Intervention 741–742
Skills Practice 743
Practice 744
Reading to Learn Mathematics 745
Enrichment 746

Lesson 12-9
Study Guide and Intervention 747–748
Skills Practice 749
Practice 750
Reading to Learn Mathematics 751
Enrichment 752

Chapter 12 Assessment
Chapter 12 Test, Form 1 753–754
Chapter 12 Test, Form 2A 755–756
Chapter 12 Test, Form 2B 757–758
Chapter 12 Test, Form 2C 759–760
Chapter 12 Test, Form 2D 761–762
Chapter 12 Test, Form 3 763–764
Chapter 12 Open-Ended Assessment 765
Chapter 12 Vocabulary Test/Review 766
Chapter 12 Quizzes 1 & 2 767
Chapter 12 Quizzes 3 & 4 768
Chapter 12 Mid-Chapter Test 769
Chapter 12 Cumulative Review 770
Chapter 12 Standardized Test Practice . 771–772
Unit 4 Test/Review (Ch. 11–12) 773–774

Standardized Test Practice
  Student Recording Sheet **A1**

ANSWERS **A2–A39**

Teacher's Guide to Using the Chapter 12 Resource Masters

The *Fast File* Chapter Resource system allows you to conveniently file the resources you use most often. The *Chapter 12 Resource Masters* includes the core materials needed for Chapter 12. These materials include worksheets, extensions, and assessment options. The answers for these pages appear at the back of this booklet.

All of the materials found in this booklet are included for viewing and printing in the *Algebra 2 TeacherWorks* CD-ROM.

Vocabulary Builder
Pages vii–viii include a student study tool that presents up to twenty of the key vocabulary terms from the chapter. Students are to record definitions and/or examples for each term. You may suggest that students highlight or star the terms with which they are not familiar.

WHEN TO USE Give these pages to students before beginning Lesson 12-1. Encourage them to add these pages to their Algebra 2 Study Notebook. Remind them to add definitions and examples as they complete each lesson.

Study Guide and Intervention
Each lesson in *Algebra 2* addresses two objectives. There is one Study Guide and Intervention master for each objective.

WHEN TO USE Use these masters as reteaching activities for students who need additional reinforcement. These pages can also be used in conjunction with the Student Edition as an instructional tool for students who have been absent.

Skills Practice
There is one master for each lesson. These provide computational practice at a basic level.

WHEN TO USE These masters can be used with students who have weaker mathematics backgrounds or need additional reinforcement.

Practice
There is one master for each lesson. These problems more closely follow the structure of the Practice and Apply section of the Student Edition exercises. These exercises are of average difficulty.

WHEN TO USE These provide additional practice options or may be used as homework for second day teaching of the lesson.

Reading to Learn Mathematics
One master is included for each lesson. The first section of each master asks questions about the opening paragraph of the lesson in the Student Edition. Additional questions ask students to interpret the context of and relationships among terms in the lesson. Finally, students are asked to summarize what they have learned using various representation techniques.

WHEN TO USE This master can be used as a study tool when presenting the lesson or as an informal reading assessment after presenting the lesson. It is also a helpful tool for ELL (English Language Learner) students.

Enrichment
There is one extension master for each lesson. These activities may extend the concepts in the lesson, offer an historical or multicultural look at the concepts, or widen students' perspectives on the mathematics they are learning. These are not written exclusively for honors students, but are accessible for use with all levels of students.

WHEN TO USE These may be used as extra credit, short-term projects, or as activities for days when class periods are shortened.

Assessment Options

The assessment masters in the *Chapter 12 Resource Masters* offer a wide range of assessment tools for intermediate and final assessment. The following lists describe each assessment master and its intended use.

Chapter Assessment

CHAPTER TESTS

- *Form 1* contains multiple-choice questions and is intended for use with basic level students.

- *Forms 2A and 2B* contain multiple-choice questions aimed at the average level student. These tests are similar in format to offer comparable testing situations.

- *Forms 2C and 2D* are composed of free-response questions aimed at the average level student. These tests are similar in format to offer comparable testing situations. Grids with axes are provided for questions assessing graphing skills.

- *Form 3* is an advanced level test with free-response questions. Grids without axes are provided for questions assessing graphing skills.

  All of the above tests include a free-response Bonus question.

- The **Open-Ended Assessment** includes performance assessment tasks that are suitable for all students. A scoring rubric is included for evaluation guidelines. Sample answers are provided for assessment.

- A **Vocabulary Test**, suitable for all students, includes a list of the vocabulary words in the chapter and ten questions assessing students' knowledge of those terms. This can also be used in conjunction with one of the chapter tests or as a review worksheet.

Intermediate Assessment

- Four free-response **quizzes** are included to offer assessment at appropriate intervals in the chapter.

- A **Mid-Chapter Test** provides an option to assess the first half of the chapter. It is composed of both multiple-choice and free-response questions.

Continuing Assessment

- The **Cumulative Review** provides students an opportunity to reinforce and retain skills as they proceed through their study of Algebra 2. It can also be used as a test. This master includes free-response questions.

- The **Standardized Test Practice** offers continuing review of algebra concepts in various formats, which may appear on the standardized tests that they may encounter. This practice includes multiple-choice, grid-in, and quantitative-comparison questions. Bubble-in and grid-in answer sections are provided on the master.

Answers

- Page A1 is an answer sheet for the Standardized Test Practice questions that appear in the Student Edition on pages 694–695. This improves students' familiarity with the answer formats they may encounter in test taking.

- The answers for the lesson-by-lesson masters are provided as reduced pages with answers appearing in red.

- Full-size answer keys are provided for the assessment masters in this booklet.

12 Reading to Learn Mathematics

Vocabulary Builder

Vocabulary Builder

This is an alphabetical list of the key vocabulary terms you will learn in Chapter 12. As you study the chapter, complete each term's definition or description. Remember to add the page number where you found the term. Add these pages to your Algebra Study Notebook to review vocabulary at the end of the chapter.

Vocabulary Term	Found on Page	Definition/Description/Example
binomial experiment		
combination		
compound event		
dependent and independent events		
inclusive events ihn·KLOO·sihv		
margin of sampling error		
measure of central tendency		
measure of variation		
mutually exclusive events MYOO·chuh·lee		
normal distribution		

(continued on the next page)

12 Reading to Learn Mathematics

Vocabulary Builder (continued)

Vocabulary Term	Found on Page	Definition/Description/Example
odds		
permutation PUHR·myoo·TAY·shuhn		
probability		
probability distribution		
random variable		
relative-frequency histogram		
sample space		
skewed distribution SKYOOD		
standard deviation		
variance VEHR·ee·uhn(t)s		

12-1 Study Guide and Intervention
The Counting Principle

Independent Events If the outcome of one event does not affect the outcome of another event and vice versa, the events are called **independent events**.

Fundamental Counting Principle	If event M can occur in m ways and is followed by event N that can occur in n ways, then the event M followed by the event N can occur in $m \cdot n$ ways.

Example FOOD For the Breakfast Special at the Country Pantry, customers can choose their eggs scrambled, fried, or poached, whole wheat or white toast, and either orange, apple, tomato, or grapefruit juice. How many different Breakfast Specials can a customer order?

A customer's choice of eggs does not affect his or her choice of toast or juice, so the events are independent. There are 3 ways to choose eggs, 2 ways to choose toast, and 4 ways to choose juice. By the Fundamental Counting Principle, there are $3 \cdot 2 \cdot 4$ or 24 ways to choose the Breakfast Special.

Exercises

Solve each problem.

1. The Palace of Pizza offers small, medium, or large pizzas with 14 different toppings available. How many different one-topping pizzas do they serve?

2. The letters A, B, C, and D are used to form four-letter passwords for entering a computer file. How many passwords are possible if letters can be repeated?

3. A restaurant serves 5 main dishes, 3 salads, and 4 desserts. How many different meals could be ordered if each has a main dish, a salad, and a dessert?

4. Marissa brought 8 T-shirts and 6 pairs of shorts to summer camp. How many different outfits consisting of a T-shirt and a pair of shorts does she have?

5. There are 6 different packages available for school pictures. The studio offers 5 different backgrounds and 2 different finishes. How many different options are available?

6. How many 5-digit even numbers can be formed using the digits 4, 6, 7, 2, 8 if digits can be repeated?

7. How many license plate numbers consisting of three letters followed by three numbers are possible when repetition is allowed?

8. How many 4-digit positive even integers are there?

Lesson 12-1

12-1 # Study Guide and Intervention *(continued)*

The Counting Principle

Dependent Events If the outcome of an event *does* affect the outcome of another event, the two events are said to be **dependent**. The Fundamental Counting Principle still applies.

Example **ENTERTAINMENT The guests at a sleepover brought 8 videos. They decided they would only watch 3 videos. How many orders of 3 different videos are possible?**

After the group chooses to watch a video, they will not choose to watch it again, so the choices of videos are dependent events.

There are 8 choices for the first video. That leaves 7 choices for the second. After they choose the first 2 videos, there are 6 remaining choices. Thus by the Fundamental Counting Principle, there are $8 \cdot 7 \cdot 6$ or 336 orders of 3 different videos.

Exercises

Solve each problem.

1. Three students are scheduled to give oral reports on Monday. In how many ways can their presentations be ordered?

2. In how many ways can the first five letters of the alphabet be arranged if each letter is used only once?

3. In how many different ways can 4 different books be arranged on the shelf?

4. How many license plates consisting of three letters followed by three numbers are possible when no repetition is allowed?

5. Sixteen teams are competing in a soccer match. Gold, silver, and bronze medals will be awarded to the top three finishers. In how many ways can the medals be awarded?

6. In a word-building game each player picks 7 letter tiles. If Julio's letters are all different, how many 3-letter combinations can he make out of his 7 letters?

7. The editor has accepted 6 articles for the news letter. In how many ways can the 6 articles be ordered?

8. There are 10 one-hour workshops scheduled for the open house at the greenhouse. There is only one conference room available. In how many ways can the workshops be ordered?

9. The top 5 runners at the cross-country meet will receive trophies. If there are 22 runners in the race, in how many ways can the trophies be awarded?

12-1 Skills Practice

The Counting Principle

State whether the events are *independent* or *dependent*.

1. finishing in first, second, or third place in a ten-person race

2. choosing a pizza size and a topping for the pizza

3. Seventy-five raffle tickets are placed in a jar. Three tickets are then selected, one after the other, without replacing a ticket after it is chosen.

4. The 232 members of the freshman class all vote by secret ballot for the class representative to the Student Senate.

Solve each problem.

5. A surveying firm plans to buy a color printer for printing its maps. It has narrowed its choice to one of three models. Each of the models is available with either 32 megabytes of random access memory (RAM), 64 megabytes of RAM, or 128 megabytes of RAM. From how many combinations of models and RAM does the firm have to choose?

6. How many arrangements of three letters can be formed from the letters of the word *MATH* if any letter will not be used more than once?

7. Allan is playing the role of Oliver in his school's production of *Oliver Twist*. The wardrobe crew has presented Allan with 5 pairs of pants and 4 shirts that he can wear. How many possible costumes consisting of a pair of pants and a shirt does Allan have to choose from?

8. The 10-member steering committee that is preparing a study of the public transportation needs of its town will select a chairperson, vice-chairperson, and secretary from the committee. No person can serve in more than one position. In how many ways can the three positions be filled?

9. Jeanine has decided to buy a pickup truck. Her choices include either a V-6 engine or a V-8 engine, a standard cab or an extended cab, and 2-wheel drive or 4-wheel drive. How many possible models does she have to choose from?

10. A mail-order company that sells gardening tools offers rakes in two different lengths. Customers can also choose either a wooden, plastic, or fiberglass handle for the rake. How many different kinds of rakes can a customer buy?

11. A Mexican restaurant offers chicken, beef, or vegetarian fajitas wrapped with either corn or flour tortillas, and topped with either mild, medium, or hot salsa. How many different choices of fajitas does a customer have?

12-1 Practice

The Counting Principle

State whether the events are *independent* or *dependent*.

1. choosing an ice cream flavor and choosing a topping for the ice cream

2. choosing an offensive player of the game and a defensive player of the game in a professional football game

3. From 15 entries in an art contest, a camp counselor chooses first, second, and third place winners.

4. Jillian is selecting two more courses for her block schedule next semester. She must select one of three morning history classes and one of two afternoon math classes.

Solve each problem.

5. A briefcase lock has 3 rotating cylinders, each containing 10 digits. How many numerical codes are possible?

6. A golf club manufacturer makes irons with 7 different shaft lengths, 3 different grips, 5 different lies, and 2 different club head materials. How many different combinations are offered?

7. There are five different routes that a commuter can take from her home to the office. In how many ways can she make a round trip if she uses a different route coming than going?

8. In how many ways can the four call letters of a radio station be arranged if the first letter must be W or K and no letters repeat?

9. How many 7-digit phone numbers can be formed if the first digit cannot be 0 or 1, and any digit can be repeated?

10. How many 7-digit phone numbers can be formed if the first digit cannot be 0, and any digit can be repeated?

11. How many 7-digit phone numbers can be formed if the first digit cannot be 0 or 1, and if no digit can be repeated?

12. How many 7-digit phone numbers can be formed if the first digit cannot be 0, and if no digit can be repeated?

13. How many 6-character passwords can be formed if the first character is a digit and the remaining 5 characters are letters that can be repeated?

14. How many 6-character passwords can be formed if the first and last characters are digits and the remaining characters are letters? Assume that any character can be repeated.

12-1 Reading to Learn Mathematics

The Counting Principle

Lesson 12-1

Pre-Activity **How can you count the maximum number of license plates a state can issue?**

Read the introduction to Lesson 12-1 at the top of page 632 in your textbook.

Assume that all Florida license plates have three letters followed by three digits, and that there are no rules against using the same letter or number more than once. How many choices are there for each letter? for each digit?

_____

Reading the Lesson

1. Shamim is signing up for her classes. Most of her classes are required, but she has two electives. For her arts class, she can chose between Art, Band, Chorus, or Drama. For her language class, she can choose between French, German, and Spanish.

   a. To organize her choices, Shamim decides to make a tree diagram. Let A, B, C, and D represent Art, Band, Chorus, and Drama, and F, G, and S represent French, German, and Spanish. Complete the following diagram.

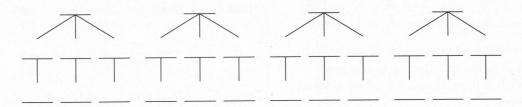

   b. How could Shamim have found the number of possible combinations without making a tree diagram?

   _____

2. A jar contains 6 red marbles, 4 blue marbles, and 3 yellow marbles. Indicate whether the events described are *dependent* or *independent*.

   a. A marble is drawn out of the jar and is not replaced. A second marble is drawn.

   _____

   b. A marble is drawn out of the jar and is put back in. The jar is shaken. A second marble is drawn.

   _____

Helping You Remember

3. One definition of *independent* is "not determined or influenced by someone or something else." How can this definition help you remember the difference between *independent* and *dependent* events?

   _____

12-1 Enrichment

Tree Diagrams and the Power Rule

If you flip a coin once, there are two possible outcomes: heads showing (H) or tails showing (T). The tree diagram to the right shows the four (2^2) possible outcomes if you flip a coin twice.

Flip 1	Flip 2	Outcomes

```
                      H      HH
              H
                      T      HT
start
                      H      TH
              T
                      T      TT
```

Example 1 Draw a tree diagram to show all the possible outcomes for flipping a coin three times. List the outcomes.

Flip 1	Flip 2	Flip 3	Outcomes

```
                          H    HHH
                 H
                          T    HHT
         H
                          H    HTH
                 T
                          T    HTT
start
                          H    THH
                 H
                          T    THT
         T
                          H    TTH
                 T
                          T    TTT
```

There are eight (2^3) possible outcomes. With each extra flip, the number of outcomes doubles. With 4 flips, there would be sixteen (2^4) outcomes.

Example 2 In a cup there are a red, a blue, and a yellow marble. How many possible outcomes are there if you draw one marble at random, replace it, and then draw another?

Draw 1	Draw 2	Outcomes

```
                       R     RR
              R        B     RB
                       Y     RY
                       R     BR
start         B        B     BB
                       Y     BY
                       R     YR
              Y        B     YB
                       Y     YY
```

There are nine (3^2) possible outcomes.

The Power Rule for the number of outcomes states that if an experiment is repeated n times, and if there are b possible outcomes each time, there are b^n total possible outcomes.

Find the total number of possible outcomes for each experiment. Use tree diagrams to help you.

1. flipping a coin 5 times

2. doing the marble experiment 6 times

3. flipping a coin 8 times

4. rolling a 6-sided die 2 times

5. rolling a 6-sided die 3 times

6. rolling a 4-sided die 2 times

7. rolling a 4-sided die 3 times

8. rolling a 12-sided die 2 times

Glencoe Algebra 2

12-2 Study Guide and Intervention

Permutations and Combinations

Permutations When a group of objects or people are arranged in a certain order, the arrangement is called a **permutation**.

Permutations	The number of permutations of n distinct objects taken r at a time is given by $P(n, r) = \dfrac{n!}{(n-r)!}$.
Permutations with Repetitions	The number of permutations of n objects of which p are alike and q are alike is $\dfrac{n!}{p!q!}$.

The rule for permutations with repetitions can be extended to any number of objects that are repeated.

Example From a list of 20 books, each student must choose 4 books for book reports. The first report is a traditional book report, the second a poster, the third a newspaper interview with one of the characters, and the fourth a timeline of the plot. How many different orderings of books can be chosen?

Since each book report has a different format, order is important. You must find the number of permutations of 20 objects taken 4 at a time.

$$P(n, r) = \frac{n!}{(n-r)!} \qquad \text{Permutation formula}$$

$$P(20, 4) = \frac{20!}{(20-4)!} \qquad n = 20, r = 4$$

$$= \frac{20!}{16!} \qquad \text{Simplify.}$$

$$= \frac{20 \cdot 19 \cdot 18 \cdot 17 \cdot \overset{1}{\cancel{16}} \cdot \overset{1}{\cancel{15}} \cdot \ldots \cdot \overset{1}{\cancel{1}}}{\underset{1}{\cancel{16}} \cdot \underset{1}{\cancel{15}} \cdot \ldots \cdot \underset{1}{\cancel{1}}} \qquad \text{Divide by common factors.}$$

$$= 116,280$$

Books for the book reports can be chosen 116,280 ways.

Lesson 12-2

Exercises

Evaluate each expression.

1. $P(6, 3)$ **2.** $P(8, 5)$ **3.** $P(9, 4)$ **4.** $P(11, 6)$

How many different ways can the letters of each word be arranged?

5. MOM **6.** MONDAY **7.** STEREO

8. SCHOOL The high school chorus has been practicing 12 songs, but there is time for only 5 of them at the spring concert. How may different orderings of 5 songs are possible?

12-2 Study Guide and Intervention *(continued)*
Permutations and Combinations

Combinations An arrangement or selection of objects in which order is *not* important is called a combination.

Combinations	The number of combinations of n distinct objects taken r at a time is given by $C(n, r) = \dfrac{n!}{(n-r)!r!}$.

Example 1 **SCHOOL How many groups of 4 students can be selected from a class of 20?**

Since the order of choosing the students is not important, you must find the number of combinations of 20 students taken 4 at a time.

$C(n, r) = \dfrac{n!}{(n-r)!r!}$ Combination formula

$C(20, 4) = \dfrac{20!}{(20-4)!4!}$ $n = 20, r = 4$

$= \dfrac{20!}{16!4!}$ or 4845

There are 4845 possible ways to choose 4 students.

Example 2 **In how many ways can you choose 1 vowel and 2 consonants from a set of 26 letter tiles? (Assume there are 5 vowels and 21 consonants.)**

By the Fundamental Counting Principle, you can multiply the number of ways to select one vowel and the number of ways to select 2 consonants. Only the letters chosen matter, not the order in which they were chosen, so use combinations.

$C(5, 1)$ One of 5 vowels are drawn.

$C(21, 2)$ Two of 21 consonants are drawn.

$C(5, 1) \cdot C(21, 2) = \dfrac{5!}{(5-1)!1!} \cdot \dfrac{21!}{(21-2)!2!}$ Combination formula

$= \dfrac{5!}{4!} \cdot \dfrac{21!}{19!2!}$ Subtract.

$= 5 \cdot 210$ or 1050   Simplify.

There are 1050 combinations of 1 vowel and 2 consonants.

Exercises

Evaluate each expression.

1. $C(5, 3)$ 2. $C(7, 4)$ 3. $C(15, 7)$ 4. $C(10, 5)$

5. **PLAYING CARDS** From a standard deck of 52 cards, in how many ways can 5 cards be drawn?

6. **HOCKEY** How many hockey teams of 6 players can be formed from 14 players without regard to position played?

7. **COMMITTEES** From a group of 10 men and 12 women, how many committees of 5 men and 6 women can be formed?

12-2 Skills Practice

Permutations and Combinations

Evaluate each expression.

1. $P(6, 3)$

2. $P(8, 2)$

3. $P(2, 1)$

4. $P(3, 2)$

5. $P(10, 4)$

6. $P(5, 5)$

7. $C(2, 2)$

8. $C(5, 3)$

9. $C(4, 1)$

10. $C(8, 7)$

11. $C(3, 2)$

12. $C(7, 4)$

Determine whether each situation involves a *permutation* or a *combination*. Then find the number of possibilities.

13. seating 8 students in 8 seats in the front row of the school auditorium

14. introducing the 5 starting players on the Woodsville High School basketball team at the beginning of the next basketball game

15. checking out 3 library books from a list of 8 books for a research paper

16. choosing 2 movies to rent from 5 movies

17. the first-, second-, and third-place finishers in a race with 10 contestants

18. electing 4 candidates to a municipal planning board from a field of 7 candidates

19. choosing 2 vegetables from a menu that offers 6 vegetable choices

20. an arrangement of the letters in the word *rhombus*

21. selecting 2 of 8 choices of orange juice at a store

22. placing a red rose bush, a yellow rose bush, a white rose bush, and a pink rose bush in a row in a planter

23. selecting 2 of 9 kittens at an animal rescue shelter

24. an arrangement of the letters in the word *isosceles*

Lesson 12-2

12-2 Practice

Permutations and Combinations

Evaluate each expression.

1. $P(8, 6)$

2. $P(9, 7)$

3. $P(3, 3)$

4. $P(4, 3)$

5. $P(4, 1)$

6. $P(7, 2)$

7. $C(8, 2)$

8. $C(11, 3)$

9. $C(20, 18)$

10. $C(9, 9)$

11. $C(3, 1)$

12. $C(9, 3) \cdot C(6, 2)$

Determine whether each situation involves a *permutation* or a *combination*. Then find the number of possibilities.

13. selecting a 4-person bobsled team from a group of 9 athletes

14. an arrangement of the letters in the word *Canada*

15. arranging 4 charms on a bracelet that has a clasp, a front, and a back

16. selecting 3 desserts from 10 desserts that are displayed on a dessert cart in a restaurant

17. an arrangement of the letters in the word *annually*

18. forming a 2-person sales team from a group of 12 salespeople

19. making 5-sided polygons by choosing any 5 of 11 points located on a circle to be the vertices

20. seating 5 men and 5 women alternately in a row, beginning with a woman

21. STUDENT GROUPS Farmington High is planning its academic festival. All math classes will send 2 representatives to compete in the math bowl. How many different groups of students can be chosen from a class of 16 students?

22. PHOTOGRAPHY A photographer is taking pictures of a bride and groom and their 6 attendants. If she takes photographs of 3 people in a group, how many different groups can she photograph?

23. AIRLINES An airline is hiring 5 flight attendants. If 8 people apply for the job, how many different groups of 5 attendants can the airline hire?

24. SUBSCRIPTIONS A school librarian would like to buy subscriptions to 7 new magazines. Her budget, however, will allow her to buy only 4 new subscriptions. How many different groups of 4 magazines can she choose from the 7 magazines?

12-2 Reading to Learn Mathematics

Permutations and Combinations

Pre-Activity **How do permutations and combinations apply to softball?**

Read the introduction to Lesson 12-2 at the top of page 638 in your textbook.

Suppose that 20 students enter a math contest. In how many ways can first, second, and third places be awarded? (Write your answer as a product. Do not calculate the product.)

Reading the Lesson

1. Indicate whether each situation involves a *permutation* or a *combination*.

   a. choosing five students from a class to work on a special project

   b. arranging five pictures in a row on a wall

   c. drawing a hand of 13 cards from a 52-card deck

   d. arranging the letters of the word *algebra*

2. Write an expression that can be used to calculate each of the following.

   a. number of combinations of n distinct objects taken r at a time

   b. number of permutations of n objects of which p are alike and q are alike

   c. number of permutations of n distinct objects taken r at a time

3. Five cards are drawn from a standard deck of cards. Suppose you are asked to determine how many possible hands consist of one heart, two diamonds, and two spades.

   a. Which of the following would you use to solve this problem: *Fundamental Counting Principle, permutations,* or *combinations*? (More than one of these may apply.)

   b. Write an expression that involves the notation $P(n, r)$ and/or $C(n, r)$ that you would use to solve this problem. (Do not do any calculations.)

Helping You Remember

4. Many students have trouble knowing when to use permutations and when to use combinations to solve counting problems. How can the idea of *order* help you to remember the difference between permutations and combinations?

12-2 **Enrichment**

Combinations and Pascal's Triangle

Pascal's triangle is a special array of numbers invented by Blaise Pascal (1623–1662). The values in Pascal's triangle can be found using the combinations shown below.

1. Evaluate the expression in each cell of the triangle.

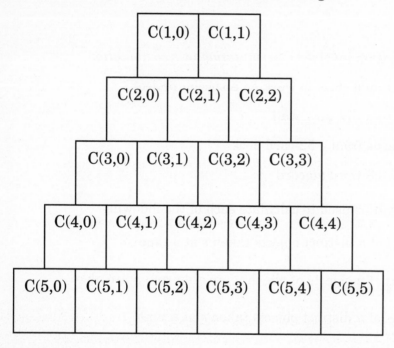

2. The pattern shows the relationship between $C(n, r)$ and Pascal's triangle. In general, it is true that $C(n, r) + C(n, r + 1) = C(n + 1, r + 1)$. Complete the proof of this property. In each step, the denominator has been given.

$$C(n, r) + C(n, r + 1) = \frac{}{r!(n - r)!} + \frac{}{(r + 1)!(n - r - 1)!}$$

$$= \frac{}{r!(n - r)!(r + 1)} + \frac{}{(r + 1)!(n - r - 1)!(n - r)}$$

$$= \frac{}{(r + 1)!(n - r)!} + \frac{}{(r + 1)!(n - r)!}$$

$$= \frac{}{(r + 1)!(n - r)!}$$

$$= \frac{}{(r + 1)!(n - r)!}$$

$$= \frac{}{(r + 1)!(n - r)!}$$

$$= \frac{}{(r + 1)![(n + 1) - (r + 1)]!}$$

$$= C(n + 1, r + 1)$$

12-3 Study Guide and Intervention
Probability

Probability and Odds In probability, a desired outcome is called a **success**; any other outcome is called a **failure**.

Probability of Success and Failure	If an event can succeed in s ways and fail in f ways, then the probabilities of success, $P(S)$, and of failure, $P(F)$, are as follows. $P(S) = \dfrac{s}{s+f}$ and $P(F) = \dfrac{f}{s+f}$.
Definition of Odds	If an event can succeed in s ways and fail in f ways, then the odds of success and of failure are as follows. Odds of success = $s{:}f$ Odds of failure = $f{:}s$

Example 1   **When 3 coins are tossed, what is the probability that at least 2 are heads?**

You can use a tree diagram to find the sample space.

First Coin	Second Coin	Third Coin	Possible Outcomes
H	H	H	HHH
		T	HHT
	T	H	HTH
		T	HTT
T	H	H	THH
		T	THT
	T	H	TTH
		T	TTT

Of the 8 possible outcomes, 4 have at least 2 heads. So the probability of tossing at least 2 heads is $\dfrac{4}{8}$ or $\dfrac{1}{2}$.

Example 2   **What is the probability of picking 4 fiction books and 2 biographies from a best-seller list that consists of 12 fiction books and 6 biographies?**

By the Fundamental Counting Principle, the number of successes is $C(12, 4) \cdot C(6, 2)$. The total number of selections, $s + f$, of 6 books is $C(18, 6)$.

$P(\text{4 fiction, 2 biography}) = \dfrac{C(12, 4) \cdot C(6, 2)}{C(18, 6)}$ or about 0.40

The probability of selecting 4 fiction books and 2 biographies is about 40%.

Exercises

Find the odds of an event occurring, given the probability of the event.

1. $\dfrac{3}{7}$ **2.** $\dfrac{4}{5}$ **3.** $\dfrac{2}{13}$ **4.** $\dfrac{1}{15}$

Find the probability of an event occurring, given the odds of the event.

5. 10:1   **6.** 2:5   **7.** 4:9   **8.** 8:3

One bag of candy contains 15 red candies, 10 yellow candies, and 6 green candies. Find the probability of each selection.

9. picking a red candy

10. not picking a yellow candy

11. picking a green candy

12. not picking a red candy

Lesson 12-3

12-3 Study Guide and Intervention *(continued)*

Probability

Probability Distributions A **random variable** is a variable whose value is the numerical outcome of a random event. A **probability distribution** for a particular random variable is a function that maps the sample space to the probabilities of the outcomes in the sample space.

Example Suppose two dice are rolled. The table and the relative-frequency histogram show the distribution of the absolute value of the difference of the numbers rolled. Use the graph to determine which outcome is the most likely. What is its probability?

Difference	0	1	2	3	4	5
Probability	$\frac{1}{6}$	$\frac{5}{18}$	$\frac{2}{9}$	$\frac{1}{6}$	$\frac{1}{9}$	$\frac{1}{18}$

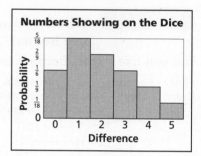

Numbers Showing on the Dice

The greatest probability in the graph is $\frac{5}{18}$.

The most likely outcome is a difference of 1 and its probability is $\frac{5}{18}$.

Exercises

Four coins are tossed.

1. Complete the table below to show the probability distribution of the number of heads.

Number of Heads	0	1	2	3	4
Probability					

2. Make relative-frequency distribution of the data.

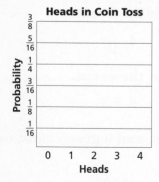

Heads in Coin Toss

12-3 Skills Practice

Probability

Ahmed is posting 2 photographs on his website. He has narrowed his choices to 4 landscape photographs and 3 portraits. If he chooses the two photographs at random, find the probability of each selection.

1. P(2 portrait)

2. P(2 landscape)

3. P(1 of each)

The Carubas have a collection of 28 video movies, including 12 westerns and 16 science fiction. Elise selects 3 of the movies at random to bring to a sleep-over at her friend's house. Find the probability of each selection.

4. P(3 westerns)

5. P(3 science fiction)

6. P(1 western and 2 science fiction)

7. P(2 westerns and 1 science fiction)

8. P(3 comedy)

9. P(2 science fiction and 2 westerns)

For Exercises 10–13, use the chart that shows the class and gender statistics for the students taking an Algebra 1 or Algebra 2 class at La Mesa High School.

If a student taking Algebra 1 or Algebra 2 is selected at random, find each probability. Express as decimals rounded to the nearest thousandth.

Class/Gender	Number
Freshman/Male	95
Freshman/Female	101
Sophomore/Male	154
Sophomore/Female	145
Junior/Male	100
Junior/Female	102

10. P(sophomore/female)

11. P(junior/male)

12. P(freshman/male)

13. P(freshman/female)

Find the odds of an event occurring, given the probability of the event.

14. $\dfrac{5}{8}$

15. $\dfrac{2}{7}$

16. $\dfrac{3}{5}$

17. $\dfrac{1}{10}$

18. $\dfrac{5}{6}$

19. $\dfrac{5}{12}$

Find the probability of an event occurring, given the odds of the event.

20. 2:1

21. 8:9

22. 4:1

23. 1:9

24. 2:7

25. 5:9

Lesson 12-3

12-3 Practice

Probability

A bag contains 1 green, 4 red, and 5 yellow balls. Two balls are selected at random. Find the probability of each selection.

1. P(2 red) **2.** P(1 red and 1 yellow) **3.** P(1 green and 1 yellow)

4. P(2 green) **5.** P(2 red and 1 yellow) **6.** P(1 red and 1 green)

A bank contains 3 pennies, 8 nickels, 4 dimes, and 10 quarters. Two coins are selected at random. Find the probability of each selection.

7. P(2 pennies) **8.** P(2 dimes) **9.** P(1 nickel and 1 dime)

10. P(1 quarter and 1 penny) **11.** P(1 quarter and 1 nickel) **12.** P(2 dimes and 1 quarter)

Henrico visits a home decorating store to choose wallpapers for his new house. The store has 28 books of wallpaper samples, including 10 books of WallPride samples and 18 books of Deluxe Wall Coverings samples. The store will allow Henrico to bring 4 books home for a few days so he can decide which wallpapers he wants to buy. If Henrico randomly chooses 4 books to bring home, find the probability of each selection.

13. P(4 WallPride) **14.** P(2 WallPride and 2 Deluxe)

15. P(1 WallPride and 3 Deluxe) **16.** P(3 WallPride and 1 Deluxe)

For Exercises 17–20, use the table that shows the range of verbal SAT scores for freshmen at a small liberal

Range	400–449	450–499	500–549	550–559	600–649	650+
Number of Students	129	275	438	602	620	412

arts college. If a freshman student is chosen at random, find each probability. Express as decimals rounded to the nearest thousandth.

17. P(400–449) **18.** P(550–559) **19.** P(at least 650)

Find the odds of an event occurring, given the probability of the event.

20. $\dfrac{4}{11}$ **21.** $\dfrac{12}{13}$ **22.** $\dfrac{5}{99}$ **23.** $\dfrac{1}{1000}$

24. $\dfrac{5}{16}$ **25.** $\dfrac{3}{95}$ **26.** $\dfrac{9}{70}$ **27.** $\dfrac{8}{15}$

Find the probability of an event occurring, given the odds of the event.

28. 2:23 **29.** 2:5 **30.** 15:1 **31.** 9:7

32. 11:14 **33.** 1000:1 **34.** 12:17 **35.** 8:13

12-3 Reading to Learn Mathematics
Probability

Pre-Activity **What do probability and odds tell you about life's risks?**

Read the introduction to Lesson 12-3 at the top of page 644 in your textbook.

What is the probability that a person will *not* be struck by lightning in a given year?

Reading the Lesson

1. Indicate whether each of the following statements is *true* or *false*.

   a. If an event can never occur, its probability is a negative number.

   b. If an event is certain to happen, its probability is 1.

   c. If an event can succeed in s ways and fail in f ways, then the probability of success is $\frac{s}{f}$.

   d. If an event can succeed in s ways and fail in f ways, then the odds against the event are $s{:}f$.

   e. A probability distribution is a function in which the domain is the sample space of an experiment.

2. A weather forecast says that the chance of rain tomorrow is 40%.

   a. Write the probability that it will rain tomorrow as a fraction in lowest terms.

   b. Write the probability that it will not rain tomorrow as a fraction in lowest terms.

   c. What are the odds in favor of rain?

   d. What are the odds against rain?

3. Refer to the table in Example 4 on page 646 in your textbook.

   a. What other sum has the same probability as a sum of 11?

   b. What are the odds of rolling a sum of 8?

   c. What are the odds against rolling a sum of 9?

Helping You Remember

4. A good way to remember something is to explain it to someone else. Suppose that your friend Roberto is having trouble remembering the difference between probability and odds. What would you tell him to help him remember this easily?

12-3 ## Enrichment

Geometric Probability

If a dart, thrown at random, hits the triangular board shown at the right, what is the chance that it will hit the shaded region? This chance, also called a probability, can be determined by comparing the area of the shaded region to the area of the board. This ratio indicates what fraction of the tosses should hit in the shaded region.

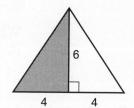

$$\frac{\text{area of shaded region}}{\text{area of triangular board}} = \frac{\frac{1}{2}(4)(6)}{\frac{1}{2}(8)(6)}$$

$$= \frac{12}{24} \text{ or } \frac{1}{2}$$

In general, if S is a subregion of some region R, then the probability, $P(S)$, that a point, chosen at random, belongs to subregion S is given by the following.

$$P(S) = \frac{\text{area of subregion } S}{\text{are of region } R}$$

Find the probability that a point, chosen at random, belongs to the shaded subregions of the following regions.

1.
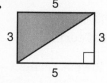

2.
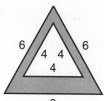

3.

The dart board shown at the right has 5 concentric circles whose centers are also the center of the square board. Each side of the board is 38 cm, and the radii of the circles are 2 cm, 5 cm, 8 cm, 11 cm, and 14 cm. A dart hitting within one of the circular regions scores the number of points indicated on the board, while a hit anywhere else scores 0 points. If a dart, thrown at random, hits the board, find the probability of scoring the indicated number of points.

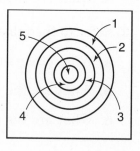

4. 0 points

5. 1 point

6. 2 points

7. 3 points

8. 4 points

9. 5 points

12-4 Study Guide and Intervention

Multiplying Probabilities

Probability of Independent Events

Probability of Two Independent Events	If two events, A and B, are independent, then the probability of both occurring is $P(A \text{ and } B) = P(A) \cdot P(B)$.

Example In a board game each player has 3 different-colored markers. To move around the board the player first spins a spinner to determine which piece can be moved. He or she then rolls a die to determine how many spaces that colored piece should move. On a given turn what is the probability that a player will be able to move the yellow piece more than 2 spaces?

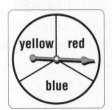

Let A be the event that the spinner lands on yellow, and let B be the event that the die shows a number greater than 2. The probability of A is $\frac{1}{3}$, and the probability of B is $\frac{2}{3}$.

$P(A \text{ and } B) = P(A) \cdot P(B)$ Probability of independent events

$\qquad = \frac{1}{3} \cdot \frac{2}{3}$ or $\frac{2}{9}$ Substitute and multiply.

The probability that the player can move the yellow piece more than 2 spaces is $\frac{2}{9}$.

Exercises

A die is rolled 3 times. Find the probability of each event.

1. a 1 is rolled, then a 2, then a 3

2. a 1 or a 2 is rolled, then a 3, then a 5 or a 6

3. 2 odd numbers are rolled, then a 6

4. a number less than 3 is rolled, then a 3, then a number greater than 3

5. A box contains 5 triangles, 6 circles, and 4 squares. If a figure is removed, replaced, and a second figure is picked, what is the probability that a triangle and then a circle will be picked?

6. A bag contains 5 red marbles and 4 white marbles. A marble is selected from the bag, then replaced, and a second selection is made. What is the probability of selecting 2 red marbles?

7. A jar contains 7 lemon jawbreakers, 3 cherry jawbreakers, and 8 rainbow jawbreakers. What is the probability of selecting 2 lemon jawbreakers in succession providing the jawbreaker drawn first is then replaced before the second is drawn?

Lesson 12-4

12-4 **Study Guide and Intervention** *(continued)*

Multiplying Probabilities

Probability of Dependent Events

Probability of Two Dependent Events	If two events, A and B, are dependent, then the probability of both events occurring is $P(A \text{ and } B) = P(A) \cdot P(B \text{ following } A)$.

Example 1 **There are 7 dimes and 9 pennies in a wallet. Suppose two coins are to be selected at random, without replacing the first one. Find the probability of picking a penny and then a dime.**

Because the coin is not replaced, the events are dependent.

Thus, $P(A \text{ and } B) = P(A) \cdot P(B \text{ following } A)$.

$P(\text{penny, then dime}) = P(\text{penny}) \cdot P(\text{dime following penny})$

$$\frac{9}{16} \cdot \frac{7}{15} = \frac{21}{80}$$

The probability is $\frac{21}{80}$ or about 0.26

Example 2 **What is the probability of drawing, without replacement, 3 hearts, then a spade from a standard deck of cards?**

Since the cards are not replaced, the events are dependent. Let H represent a heart and S represent a spade.

$P(\text{H, H, H, S}) = P(\text{H}) \cdot P(\text{H following H}) \cdot P(\text{H following 2 Hs}) \cdot P(\text{S following 3 Hs})$

$$= \frac{13}{52} \cdot \frac{12}{51} \cdot \frac{11}{50} \cdot \frac{13}{49} \text{ or about } 0.003$$

The probability is about 0.003 of drawing 3 hearts, then a spade.

Exercises

Find each probability.

1. The cup on Sophie's desk holds 4 red pens and 7 black pens. What is the probability of her selecting first a black pen, then a red one?

2. What is the probability of drawing two cards showing odd numbers from a set of cards that show the first 20 counting numbers if the first card is not replaced before the second is chosen?

3. There are 3 quarters, 4 dimes, and 7 nickels in a change purse. Suppose 3 coins are selected without replacement. What is the probability of selecting a quarter, then a dime, and then a nickel?

4. A basket contains 4 plums, 6 peaches, and 5 oranges. What is the probability of picking 2 oranges, then a peach if 3 pieces of fruit are selected at random?

5. A photographer has taken 8 black and white photographs and 10 color photographs for a brochure. If 4 photographs are selected at random, what is the probability of picking first 2 black and white photographs, then 2 color photographs?

12-4 Skills Practice

Multiplying Probabilities

A die is rolled twice. Find each probability.

1. P(5, then 6)

2. P(no 2s)

3. P(two 1s)

4. P(any number, then not 5)

5. P(4, then not 6)

6. P(not 1, then not 2)

A board game uses a set of 6 different cards. Each card displays one of the following figures: a star, a square, a circle, a diamond, a rectangle, or a pentagon. The cards are placed face down, and a player chooses two cards. Find each probability.

7. P(circle, then star), if no replacement occurs

8. P(diamond, then square), if replacement occurs

9. P(2 polygons), if replacement occurs

10. P(2 polygons), if no replacement occurs

11. P(circle, then hexagon), if no replacement occurs

Determine whether the events are *independent* or *dependent*. Then find each probability.

12. A mixed box of herbal teabags contains 2 lemon teabags, 3 orange-mango teabags, 3 chamomile teabags, and 1 apricot-ginger teabag. Kevin chooses 2 teabags at random to bring to work with him. What is the probability that he first chooses a lemon teabag and then a chamomile teabag?

13. The chart shows the selection of olive oils that Hasha finds in a specialty foods catalog. If she randomly selects one type of oil, then randomly selects another, different oil, what is the probability that both selections are domestic, first cold pressed oils?

Type of Oil	Domestic	Imported
Pure	2	5
Cold Pressed	4	8
First Cold Pressed	7	15

For Exercises 14 and 15, two thirds of the area of the spinner earns you 50 points. Suppose you spin the spinner twice.

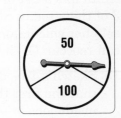

14. Sketch a tree diagram showing all of the possibilities. Use it to find the probability of spinning 50 points, then 100 points.

15. What is the probability that you get 100 points on each spin?

Lesson 12-4

12-4 Practice

Multiplying Probabilities

A die is rolled three times. Find each probability.

1. P(three 4s)

2. P(no 4s)

3. P(2, then 3, then 1)

4. P(three different even numbers)

5. P(any number, then 5, then 5)

6. P(even number, then odd number, then 1)

There are 3 nickels, 2 dimes, and 5 quarters in a purse. Three coins are selected in succession at random. Find the probability.

7. P(nickel, then dime, then quarter), if no replacement occurs

8. P(nickel, then dime, then quarter), if replacement occurs

9. P(2 nickels, then 1 quarter), if no replacement occurs

10. P(3 dimes), if replacement occurs

11. P(3 dimes), if no replacement occurs

For Exercises 12 and 13, determine whether the events are *independent* or *dependent*. Then find each probability.

12. Serena is creating a painting. She wants to use 2 more colors. She chooses randomly from 6 shades of red, 10 shades of green, 4 shades of yellow, 4 shades of purple, and 6 shades of blue. What is the probability that she chooses 2 shades of green?

13. Kershel's mother is shopping at a bakery. The owner offers Kershel a cookie from a jar containing 22 chocolate chip cookies, 18 sugar cookies, and 15 oatmeal cookies. Without looking, Kershel selects one, drops it back in, and then randomly selects another. What is the probability that neither selection was a chocolate chip cookie?

14. **METEOROLOGY** The Fadeeva's are planning a 3-day vacation to the mountains. A long-range forecast reports that the probability of rain each day is 10%. Assuming that the daily probabilities of rain are independent, what is the probability that there is no rain on the first two days, but that it rains on the third day?

RANDOM NUMBERS For Exercises 15 and 16, use the following information.

Anita has a list of 20 jobs around the house to do, and plans to do 3 of them today. She assigns each job a number from 1 to 20, and sets her calculator to generate random numbers from 1 to 20, which can reoccur. Of the jobs, 3 are outside, and the rest are inside.

15. Sketch a tree diagram showing all of the possibilities that the first three numbers generated correspond to inside jobs or outside jobs. Use it to find the probability that the first two numbers correspond to inside jobs, and the third to an outside job.

16. What is the probability that the number generated corresponds to an outside job three times in a row?

12-4 Reading to Learn Mathematics

Multiplying Probabilities

Pre-Activity **How does probability apply to basketball?**

Read the introduction to Lesson 12-4 at the top of page 651 in your textbook.

Write the probability that Reggie Miller made a free-throw shot during the 1998–99 season as a fraction in lowest terms. (Your answer should not include a decimal.)

Reading the Lesson

1. A bag contains 4 yellow balls, 5 red balls, 1 white ball, and 2 black balls. A ball is drawn from the bag and is not replaced. A second ball is drawn.

   a. Let Y be the event "first ball is yellow" and B be the event "second ball is black." Are these events *independent* or *dependent*?

   b. Tell which formula you would use to find the probability that the first ball is yellow and the second ball is black.

   A. $P(Y \text{ and } B) = \dfrac{P(Y)}{P(Y) + P(B)}$

   B. $P(Y \text{ and } B) = P(Y) \cdot P(B)$

   C. $P(Y \text{ and } B) = P(Y) \cdot P(B \text{ following } Y)$

   c. Which equation shows the correct calculation of this probability?

   A. $\dfrac{1}{3} + \dfrac{2}{11} = \dfrac{17}{33}$ **B.** $\dfrac{1}{3} \cdot \dfrac{2}{11} = \dfrac{2}{33}$

   C. $\dfrac{1}{3} + \dfrac{1}{6} = \dfrac{1}{2}$ **D.** $\dfrac{1}{3} \cdot \dfrac{1}{6} = \dfrac{1}{18}$

   d. Which equation shows the correct calculation of the probability that if three balls are drawn in succession without replacement, all three will be red?

   A. $\dfrac{5}{12} \cdot \dfrac{5}{12} \cdot \dfrac{5}{12} = \dfrac{125}{1728}$ **B.** $\dfrac{5}{12} \cdot \dfrac{4}{11} \cdot \dfrac{3}{10} = \dfrac{1}{22}$

   C. $\dfrac{5}{12} + \dfrac{4}{11} + \dfrac{3}{10} = \dfrac{713}{660}$

Helping You Remember

2. Some students have trouble remembering a lot of formulas, so they try to keep the number of formulas they have to know to a minimum. Can you learn just one formula that will allow you to find probabilities for both independent and dependent events? Explain your reasoning.

     721   *Glencoe Algebra 2*

Lesson 12-4

12-4 **Enrichment**

Conditional Probability

Suppose a pair of dice is thrown. It is known that the sum is greater than seven. Find the probability that the dice match.

The probability of an event given the occurrence of another event is called *conditional probability*. The conditional probability of event A, the dice match, given event B, their sum is greater than seven, is denoted $P(A/B)$.

There are 15 sums greater than seven and there are 36 possible pairs altogether.

$P(B) = \dfrac{15}{36}$

There are three matching pairs greater than seven.

$P(A \text{ and } B) = \dfrac{3}{36}$

$P(A/B) = \dfrac{P(A \text{ and } B)}{P(B)}$

$P(A/B) = \dfrac{\frac{3}{36}}{\frac{15}{36}}$ or $\dfrac{1}{5}$

The conditional probability is $\dfrac{1}{5}$.

A card is drawn from a standard deck of 52 and is found to be red. Given that event, find each of the following probabilities.

1. $P(\text{heart})$

2. $P(\text{ace})$

3. $P(\text{face card})$

4. $P(\text{jack or ten})$

5. $P(\text{six of spades})$

6. $P(\text{six of hearts})$

A sports survey taken at Stirers High School shows that 48% of the respondents liked soccer, 66% liked basketball, and 38% liked hockey. Also, 30% liked soccer and basketball, 22% liked basketball and hockey and 28% liked soccer and hockey. Finally, 12% liked all three sports. Find each of the following probabilities.

7. The probability Meg likes soccer if she likes basketball.

8. The probability Biff likes basketball if he likes soccer.

9. The probability Muffy likes hockey if she likes basketball.

10. The probability Greg likes hockey and basketball if he likes soccer.

Glencoe Algebra 2

12-5 Study Guide and Intervention

Adding Probabilities

Mutually Exclusive Events Events that cannot occur at the same time are called mutually exclusive events.

Probability of Mutually Exclusive Events	If two events, A and B, are mutually exclusive, then $P(A \text{ or } B) = P(A) + P(B)$.

This formula can be extended to any number of mutually exclusive events.

Example 1 To choose an afternoon activity, summer campers pull slips of paper out of a hat. Today there are 25 slips for a nature walk, 35 slips for swimming, and 30 slips for arts and crafts. What is the probability that a camper will pull a slip for a nature walk or for swimming?

These are mutually exclusive events. Note that there is a total of 90 slips.

$P(\text{nature walk or swimming}) = P(\text{nature walk}) + P(\text{swimming})$
$$= \frac{25}{90} + \frac{35}{90} \text{ or } \frac{2}{3}$$

The probability of a camper's pulling out a slip for a nature walk or for swimming is $\frac{2}{3}$.

Example 2 By the time one tent of 6 campers gets to the front of the line, there are only 10 nature walk slips and 15 swimming slips left. What is the probability that more than 4 of the 6 campers will choose a swimming slip?

$P(\text{more than 4 swimmers}) = P(5 \text{ swimmers}) + P(6 \text{ swimmers})$
$$= \frac{C(10, 1) \cdot C(15, 5)}{C(25, 6)} + \frac{C(10, 0) \cdot C(15, 6)}{C(25, 6)}$$
$$\approx 0.2$$

The probability of more than 4 of the campers swimming is about 0.2.

Exercises

Find each probability.

1. A bag contains 45 dyed eggs: 15 yellow, 12 green, and 18 red. What is the probability of selecting a green or a red egg?

2. The letters from the words LOVE and LIVE are placed on cards and put in a box. What is the probability of selecting an L or an O from the box?

3. A pair of dice is rolled, and the two numbers are added. What is the probability that the sum is either a 5 or a 7?

4. A bowl has 10 whole wheat crackers, 16 sesame crackers, and 14 rye crisps. If a person picks a cracker at random, what is the probability of picking either a sesame cracker or a rye crisp?

5. An art box contains 12 colored pencils and 20 pastels. If 5 drawing implements are chosen at random, what is the probability that at least 4 of them are pastels?

Lesson 12-5

12-5 Study Guide and Intervention *(continued)*

Adding Probabilities

Inclusive Events

Probability of Inclusive Events	If two events, *A* and *B*, are inclusive, $P(A \text{ or } B) = P(A) + P(B) - P(A \text{ and } B)$.

Example **What is the probability of drawing a face card or a black card from a standard deck of cards?**

The two events are inclusive, since a card can be both a face card and a black card.

$P(\text{face card or black card}) = P(\text{face card}) + P(\text{black card}) - P(\text{black face card})$

$$= \frac{3}{13} + \frac{1}{2} - \frac{3}{26}$$

$$= \frac{8}{13} \text{ or about } 0.62$$

The probability of drawing either a face card or a black card is about 0.62

Exercises

Find each probability.

1. What is the probability of drawing a red card or an ace from a standard deck of cards?

2. Three cards are selected from a standard deck of 52 cards. What is the probability of selecting a king, a queen, or a red card?

3. The letters of the alphabet are placed in a bag. What is the probability of selecting a vowel or one of the letters from the word QUIZ?

4. A pair of dice is rolled. What is the probability that the sum is odd or a multiple of 3?

5. The Venn diagram at the right shows the number of juniors on varsity sports teams at Elmwood High School. Some athletes are on varsity teams for one season only, some athletes for two seasons, and some for all three seasons. If a varsity athlete is chosen at random from the junior class, what is the probability that he or she plays a fall or winter sport?

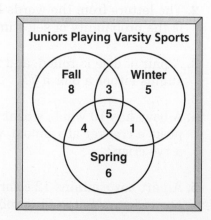

Juniors Playing Varsity Sports

Fall 8   3   Winter 5

5

4   1

Spring 6

12-5 **Skills Practice**

Adding Probabilities

Eli has 10 baseball cards of 10 different players in his pocket. Three players are pitchers, 5 are outfielders, and 2 are catchers. If Eli randomly selects a card to trade, find each probability.

1. *P*(pitcher or outfielder)   **2.** *P*(pitcher or catcher)   **3.** *P*(outfielder or catcher)

A die is rolled. Find each probability.

4. *P*(5 or 6)   **5.** *P*(at least a 3)   **6.** *P*(less than 4)

Determine whether the events are *mutually exclusive* or *inclusive*. Then find the probability.

7. A die is rolled. What is the probability of rolling a 3 or a 4?

8. A die is rolled. What is the probability of rolling an even number or a 4?

9. A card is drawn from a standard deck of cards. What is the probability of drawing a king or a queen?

10. A card is drawn from a standard deck of cards. What is the probability of drawing a jack or a heart?

11. The sophomore class is selling Mother's Day plants to raise money. Susan's prize for being the top seller of plants is a choice of a book, a CD, or a video. She can choose from 6 books, 3 CDs, and 5 videos. What is the probability that Susan selects a book or a CD?

A spinner numbered 1–10 is spun. Find each probability.

12. *P*(less than 5 or even)   **13.** *P*(even or odd)   **14.** *P*(prime or even)

Two cards are drawn from a standard deck of cards. Find each probability.

15. *P*(both red or both black)   **16.** *P*(both aces or both red)

17. *P*(both 2s or both less than 5)   **18.** *P*(both black or both less than 5)

For Exercises 19 and 20, use the Venn diagram that shows the number of participants in two different kinds of aerobic exercise classes that are offered at a health club. Determine each probability if a person is selected at random from the participants.

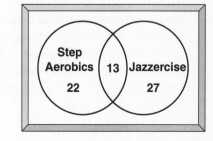

19. *P*(step aerobics or jazzercise, but not both)

20. *P*(step aerobics and jazzercise)

Lesson 12-5

12-5 Practice

Adding Probabilities

An urn contains 7 white marbles and 5 blue marbles. Four marbles are selected without replacement. Find each probability.

1. P(4 white or 4 blue) **2.** P(exactly 3 white) **3.** P(at least 3 white)

4. P(fewer than 3 white) **5.** P(3 white or 3 blue) **6.** P(no white or no blue)

Jason and Maria are playing a board game in which three dice are tossed to determine a player's move. Find each probability.

7. P(two 5s) **8.** P(three 5s) **9.** P(at least two 5s)

10. P(no 5s) **11.** P(one 5) **12.** P(one 5 or two 5s)

Determine whether the events are *mutually exclusive* or *inclusive*. Then find the probability.

13. A clerk chooses 4 CD players at random for floor displays from a shipment of 24 CD players. If 15 of the players have a blue case and the rest have a red case, what is the probability of choosing 4 players with a blue case or 4 players with a red case?

14. A department store employs 28 high school students, all juniors and seniors. Six of the 12 seniors are females and 12 of the juniors are males. One student employee is chosen at random. What is the probability of selecting a senior or a female?

15. A restaurant has 5 pieces of apple pie, 4 pieces of chocolate cream pie, and 3 pieces of blueberry pie. If Janine selects a piece of pie at random for dessert, what is the probability that she selects either apple or chocolate cream?

16. At a statewide meeting, there are 20 school superintendents, 13 principals, and 6 assistant principals. If one of these people is chosen at random, what is the probability that he or she is either a principal or an assistant principal?

17. An airline has one bank of 13 telephones at a reservations office. Of the 13 operators who work there, 8 take reservations for domestic flights and 5 take reservations for international flights. Seven of the operators taking domestic reservations and 3 of the operators taking international reservations are female. If an operator is chosen at random, what is the probability that the person chosen takes domestic reservations or is a male?

18. MUSIC Forty senior citizens were surveyed about their music preferences. The results are displayed in the Venn diagram. If a senior citizen from the survey group is selected at random, what is the probability that he or she likes only country and western music? What is the probability that he or she likes classical and/or country, but not 1940's pop?

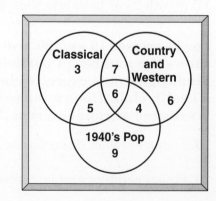

12-5 Reading to Learn Mathematics

Adding Probabilities

Pre-Activity **How does probability apply to your personal habits?**

Read the introduction to Lesson 12-5 at the top of page 658 in your textbook.

Why do the percentages shown on the bar graph add up to more than 100%?

_____

_____

Reading the Lesson

1. Indicate whether the events in each pair are *inclusive* or *mutually exclusive*.

   a. *Q*: drawing a queen from a standard deck of cards
   D: drawing a diamond from a standard deck of cards

   b. *J*: drawing a jack from a standard deck of cards
   K: drawing a king from a standard deck of cards

2. Marla took a quiz on this lesson that contained the following problem.

   Each of the integers from 1 through 25 is written on a slip of paper and placed in an envelope. If one slip is drawn at random, what is the probability that it is odd or a multiple of 5?

   Here is Marla's work.

   $$P(\text{odd}) = \frac{13}{25} \qquad P(\text{multiple of 5}) = \frac{5}{25} \text{ or } \frac{1}{5}$$

   $$P(\text{odd or multiple of 5}) = P(\text{odd}) + P(\text{multiple of 5})$$

   $$= \frac{13}{25} + \frac{5}{25} = \frac{18}{25}$$

   a. Why is Marla's work incorrect?

   _____

   _____

   b. Show the corrected work.

Helping You Remember

3. Some students have trouble remembering a lot of formulas, so they try to keep the number of formulas they have to know to a minimum. Can you learn just one formula that will allow you to find probabilities for both mutually exclusive and inclusive events? Explain your reasoning.

   _____

Lesson 12-5

12-5 Enrichment

Probability and Tic-Tac-Toe

What would be the chances of winning at tic-tac-toe if it were turned into a game of pure chance? To find out, the nine cells of the tic-tac-toe board are numbered from 1 to 9 and nine chips (also numbered from 1 to 9) are put into a bag. Player A draws a chip at random and enters an X in the corresponding cell. Player B does the same and enters an O.

To solve the problem, assume that both players draw all their chips without looking and all X and O entries are made at the same time. There are four possible outcomes: a draw, A wins, B wins, and either A or B can win.

There are 16 arrangements that result in a draw. Reflections and rotations must be counted as shown below.

```
O X O       X O X       O O X
X O X  4    O O X  4    X X O  8
X O X       X X O       O X X
```

There are 36 arrangements in which either player may win because both players have winning triples.

```
X X X       X X X       X O X       X X X       X X X       X X O
O O O  4    X O X  4    X X X  4    X X O  8    O O O  8    X X X  8
X O X       O O O       O O O       O O O       X X O       O O O
```

In these 36 cases, A's chances of winning are $\frac{13}{40}$.

1. Find the 12 arrangements in which B wins and A cannot.

2. Below are 12 of the arrangements in which A wins and B cannot. Write the numbers to show the reflections and rotations for each arrangement. What is the total number?

```
O X O       X O X       X X X       X X X       X O O       X O O
X X X       O X O       X O O       O X O       X X X       X X O
O X O       X O X       X O O       O X O       O O X       O O X


X X O       X X X       X X X       X X X       X O O       X X O
O X X       O X O       X O O       X O O       X X X       O X O
O O X       O O X       O X O       O O X       O X O       X O X
```

3. There are $\frac{9!}{(5!4!)}$ different and equally probable distributions. Complete the chart to find the probability for a draw or for A or B to win.

Draw: $\frac{16}{126}$	=	_____
A wins: _____	$+ \frac{13}{40}\left(\frac{36}{126}\right) =$	_____
B wins: _____	$+$ _____	= _____

12-6 Study Guide and Intervention

Statistical Measures

Measures of Central Tendency

Measures of Central Tendency	Use	When
	mean	the data are spread out and you want an average of values
	median	the data contain outliers
	mode	the data are tightly clustered around one or two values

Example **Find the mean, median, and mode of the following set of data: {42, 39, 35, 40, 38, 35, 45}.**

To find the mean, add the values and divide by the number of values.

$$\text{mean} = \frac{42 + 39 + 35 + 40 + 38 + 35 + 45}{7} \approx 39.14.$$

To find the median, arrange the values in ascending or descending order and choose the middle value. (If there is an even number of values, find the mean of the two middle values.) In this case, the median is 39.

To find the mode, take the most common value. In this case, the mode is 35.

Exercises

Find the mean, median, and mode of each set of data. Round to the nearest hundredth, if necessary.

1. {238, 261, 245, 249, 255, 262, 241, 245}

2. {9, 13, 8, 10, 11, 9, 12, 16, 10, 9}

3. {120, 108, 145, 129, 102, 132, 134, 118, 108, 142}

4. {68, 54, 73, 58, 63, 72, 65, 70, 61}

5. {34, 49, 42, 38, 40, 45, 34, 28, 43, 30}

6. The table at the right shows the populations of the six New England capitals. Which would be the most appropriate measure of central tendency to represent the data? Explain why and find that value.

Source: www.factfinder.census.gov

City	Population (rounded to the nearest 1000)
Augusta, ME	19,000
Boston, MA	589,000
Concord, NH	37,000
Hartford, CT	122,000
Montpelier, VT	8,000
Providence, RI	174,000

12-6 Study Guide and Intervention (continued)

Statistical Measures

Measures of Variation The *range* and the **standard deviation** measure how scattered a set of data is.

Standard Deviation	If a set of data consists of the *n* values $x_1, x_2, ..., x_n$ and has mean $\bar{x}$, then the standard deviation is given by $\sigma = \sqrt{\dfrac{(x_1 - \bar{x})^2 + (x_2 - \bar{x})^2 + ... + (x_n - \bar{x})^2}{n}}$.

The square of the standard deviation is called the **variance**.

Example Find the variance and standard deviation of the data set {10, 9, 6, 9, 18, 4, 8, 20}.

Step 1 Find the mean.

$$\bar{x} = \frac{10 + 9 + 6 + 9 + 18 + 4 + 8 + 20}{8} = 10.5$$

Step 2 Find the variance.

$$\sigma^2 = \frac{(x_1 - \bar{x})^2 + (x_2 - \bar{x})^2 + ... + (x_n - \bar{x})^2}{n} \qquad \text{Standard variance formula}$$

$$= \frac{(10 - 10.5)^2 + (9 - 10.5)^2 + ... + (20 - 10.5)^2}{8}$$

$$= \frac{220}{8} \text{ or } 27.5$$

Step 3 Find the standard deviation.

$$\sigma = \sqrt{27.5}$$

$$\approx 5.2$$

The variance is 27.5 and the standard deviation is about 5.2.

Exercises

Find the variance and standard deviation of each set of data. Round to the nearest tenth.

1. {100, 89, 112, 104, 96, 108, 93}

2. {62, 54, 49, 62, 48, 53, 50}

3. {8, 9, 8, 8, 9, 7, 8, 9, 6}

4. {4.2, 5.0, 4.7, 4.5, 5.2, 4.8, 4.6, 5.1}

5. The table at the right lists the prices of ten brands of breakfast cereal. What is the standard deviation of the values to the nearest penny?

Price of 10 Brands of Breakfast Cereal	
$2.29	$3.19
$3.39	$2.79
$2.99	$3.09
$3.19	$2.59
$2.79	$3.29

12-6 Skills Practice

Statistical Measures

Find the variance and standard deviation of each set of data to the nearest tenth.

1. {32, 41, 35, 35, 46, 42}

2. {13, 62, 77, 24, 38, 19, 88}

3. {89, 99, 42, 16, 42, 71, 16}

4. {450, 400, 625, 225, 300, 750, 650, 625}

5. {17, 23, 65, 94, 33, 33, 33, 8, 57, 75, 44, 12, 11, 68, 39}

6. {7.2, 3.1, 3.8, 9.5, 8.3, 8.4}

7. {1.5, 2.5, 3.5, 4.5, 4.5, 5.5, 6.5, 7.5}

For Exercises 8 and 9, use the table that shows the profit in billions of dollars reported by U.S. manufacturers for the first quarter of the years from 1997 through 2001.

Year	1997	1998	1999	2000	2001
Seasonally-Adjusted Profit ($ billions)	$61.4	$75.6	$60.9	$78.5	$45.3

Source: U. S. Census Bureau

8. Find the mean and median of the data to the nearest tenth.

9. Which measure of central tendency best represents the data? Explain.

For Exercises 10 and 11, use the table that shows the percent of fourth grade students reading at or above the proficiency level in a nationally-administered reading assessment.

Year	1992	1994	1998	2000
Percent at or above proficiency level	29%	30%	31%	32%

Source: National Center for Education Statistics

10. Find the mean, median, and standard deviation of the data to the nearest tenth.

11. What do the statistics from Exercise 11 tell you about the data?

Glencoe Algebra 2

12-6 Practice

Statistical Measures

Find the variance and standard deviation of each set of data to the nearest tenth.

1. {47, 61, 93, 22, 82, 22, 37}

2. {10, 10, 54, 39, 96, 91, 91, 18}

3. {1, 2, 2, 3, 3, 3, 4, 4, 4, 4, 5, 5, 5, 5, 5}

4. {1100, 725, 850, 335, 700, 800, 950}

5. {3.4, 7.1, 8.5, 5.1, 4.7, 6.3, 9.9, 8.4, 3.6}

6. {2.8, 0.5, 1.9, 0.8, 1.9, 1.5, 3.3, 2.6, 0.7, 2.5}

7. HEALTH CARE Eight physicians with 15 patients on a hospital floor see these patients an average of 18 minutes a day. The 22 nurses on the same floor see the patients an average of 3 hours a day. As a hospital administrator, would you quote the mean, median, or mode as an indicator of the amount of daily medical attention the patients on this floor receive? Explain.

For Exercises 8–10, use the frequency table that shows the percent of public school teachers in the U. S. in 1999 who used computers or the Internet at school for various administrative and teaching activities.

Activity	Percent Using Computer or Internet
Create instructional materials	39
Administrative record keeping	34
Communicate with colleagues	23
Gather information for planning lessons	16
Multimedia classroom presentations	8
Access research and best practices for teaching	8
Communicate with parents or students	8
Access model lesson plans	6

8. Find the mean, median, and mode of the data.

9. Suppose you believe teachers use computers or the Internet too infrequently. Which measure would you quote as the "average?" Explain.

Source: National Assessment of Educational Progress

10. Suppose you believe teachers use computers or the Internet too often. Which measure would you quote as the "average?" Explain.

For Exercises 11 and 12, use the frequency table that shows the number of games played by 24 American League baseball players between opening day, 2001 and September 8, 2001.

11. Find the mean, median, mode, and standard deviation of the number of games played to the nearest tenth.

12. For how many players is the number of games within one standard deviation of the mean?

No. of Games	Frequency
141	4
140	3
139	4
138	5
137	2
136	3
135	3

Source: Major League Baseball

12-6 Reading to Learn Mathematics

Statistical Measures

Pre-Activity **What statistics should a teacher tell the class after a test?**

Read the introduction to Lesson 12-6 at the top of page 664 in your textbook.

There is more than one way to give an "average" score for this test. Three measures of central tendency for these scores are 94, 76.5 and 73.9. Can you tell which of these is the mean, the median, and the mode without doing any calculations? Explain your answer.

Reading the Lesson

1. Match each measure with one of the six descriptions of how to find measures of central tendency and variation.

   a. median   **b.** mode   **c.** range

   d. variance   **e.** mean   **f.** standard deviation

   i. Find the most commonly occurring values or values in a set of data.

   ii. Add the data and divide by the number of items.

   iii. Find the mean of the squares of the differences between each value in the set of data and the mean.

   iv. Find the difference between the largest and smallest values in the set of data.

   v. Take the positive square root of the variance.

   vi. If there is an odd number of items in a set of data, take the middle one. If there is an even number of items, add the two middle items and divide by 2.

Helping You Remember

2. It is usually easier to remember a complicated procedure if you break it down into steps. Write the procedure for finding the standard deviation for a set of data in a series of brief, numbered steps.

12-6 **Enrichment**

Probabilities in Genetics

Genes are the units which transmit hereditary traits. The possible forms which a gene may take, **dominant** and **recessive,** are called **alleles.** A particular trait is determined by two alleles, one from the female parent and one from the male parent. If an organism has the trait which is dominant, it may have either two dominant alleles or one dominant and one recessive allele. If the organism has the trait which is recessive, it must have two recessive alleles.

Example **Consider a plant in which tall stems, *T*, are dominant to short stems, *t*. What is the probability of obtaining a long-stemmed plant if two long-stemmed plants both with the genetic formula *Tt* are crossed?**

	T	*t*
T	*TT*	*Tt*
t	*Tt*	*tt*

A *Punnett square* is a chart used to determine the possible combinations of characteristics among offspring.

   3 tall-stemmed
+ 1 short-stemmed
   4 total

Thus, the probability is $\frac{3}{4}$.

In a certain plant, red flowers, *R*, are dominant to white flowers, *r*. If a white-flowered plant, *rr* is crossed with a red-flowered plant, *Rr*, find the probability of each of the following.

1. white-flowered plant

2. red-flowered plant

In a certain plant, tall, *T*, is dominant to short, *t*, and green pods, *G*, are dominant to yellow pods, *g*. Plants with the genetic formulas *TtGg* and *TTGg* are crossed. Find the probability of each of the following.

3. tall plant with green pods

4. tall plant with yellow pods

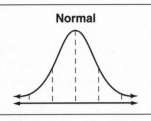

12-7 Study Guide and Intervention

The Normal Distribution

Normal and Skewed Distributions A **continuous probability** distribution is represented by a curve.

Types of Continuous Distributions	Normal 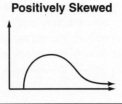	Positively Skewed 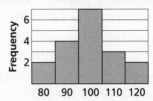	Negatively Skewed 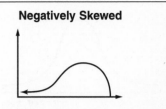

Example **Determine whether the data below appear to be *positively skewed*, *negatively skewed*, or *normally distributed*.**
{100, 120, 110, 100, 110, 80, 100, 90, 100, 120, 100, 90, 110, 100, 90, 80, 100, 90}

Make a frequency table for the data.

Value	80	90	100	110	120
Frequency	2	4	7	3	2

Then use the data to make a histogram.

Since the histogram is roughly symmetric, the data appear to be normally distributed.

Exercises

Determine whether the data in each table appear to be *positively skewed*, *negatively skewed*, or *normally distributed*. Make a histogram of the data.

1. {27, 24, 29, 25, 27, 22, 24, 25, 29, 24, 25, 22, 27, 24, 22, 25, 24, 22}

2.

Shoe Size	4	5	6	7	8	9	10
No. of Students	1	2	4	8	5	1	2

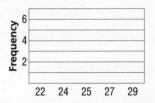

3.

Housing Price	No. of Houses Sold
less than $100,000	0
$100,00–$120,000	1
$121,00–$140,000	3
$141,00–$160,000	7
$161,00–$180,000	8
$181,00–$200,000	6
over $200,000	12

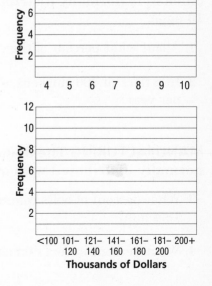

12-7 Study Guide and Intervention *(continued)*

The Normal Distribution

Use Normal Distributions

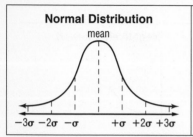	Normal distributions have these properties. The graph is maximized at the mean. The mean, median, and mode are about equal. About 68% of the values are within one standard deviation of the mean. About 95% of the values are within two standard deviations of the mean. About 99% of the values are within three standard deviations of the mean.

Example The heights of players in a basketball league are normally distributed with a mean of 6 feet 1 inch and a standard deviation of 2 inches.

a. What is the probability that a player selected at random will be shorter than 5 feet 9 inches?

Draw a normal curve. Label the mean and the mean plus or minus multiples of the standard deviation.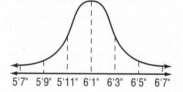

The value of 5 feet 9 inches is 2 standard deviations below the mean, so approximately 2.5% of the players will be shorter than 5 feet 9 inches.

b. If there are 240 players in the league, about how many players are taller than 6 feet 3 inches?

The value of 6 feet 3 inches is one standard deviation above the mean. Approximately 16% of the players will be taller than this height.

$240 \times 0.16 \approx 38$

About 38 of the players are taller than 6 feet 3 inches.

Exercises

EGG PRODUCTION The number of eggs laid per year by a particular breed of chicken is normally distributed with a mean of 225 and a standard deviation of 10 eggs.

1. About what percent of the chickens will lay between 215 and 235 eggs per year?

2. In a flock of 400 chickens, about how many would you expect to lay more than 245 eggs per year?

MANUFACTURING The diameter of bolts produced by a manufacturing plant is normally distributed with a mean of 18 mm and a standard deviation of 0.2 mm.

3. What percent of bolts coming off of the assembly line have a diameter greater than 18.4 mm?

4. What percent have a diameter between 17.8 and 18.2 mm?

12-7 Skills Practice

The Normal Distribution

Lesson 12-7

Determine whether the data in each table appear to be *positively skewed*, *negatively skewed*, or *normally distributed*.

1.

Miles Run	Track Team Members
0–4	3
5–9	4
10–14	7
15–19	5
20–23	2

2.

Speeches Given	Political Candidates
0–5	1
6–11	2
12–17	3
18–23	8
24–29	8

For Exercises 3 and 4, use the frequency table that shows the average number of days patients spent on the surgical ward of a hospital last year.

Days	Number of Patients
0–3	5
4–7	18
8–11	11
12–15	9
16+	6

3. Make a histogram of the data.

4. Do the data appear to be *positively skewed*, *negatively skewed*, or *normally distributed*? Explain.

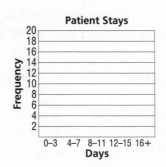

DELIVERY For Exercises 5–7, use the following information.

The time it takes a bicycle courier to deliver a parcel to his farthest customer is normally distributed with a mean of 40 minutes and a standard deviation of 4 minutes.

5. About what percent of the courier's trips to this customer take between 36 and 44 minutes?

6. About what percent of the courier's trips to this customer take between 40 and 48 minutes?

7. About what percent of the courier's trips to this customer take less than 32 minutes?

TESTING For Exercises 8–10, use the following information.

The average time it takes sophomores to complete a math test is normally distributed with a mean of 63.3 minutes and a standard deviation of 12.3 minutes.

8. About what percent of the sophomores take more than 75.6 minutes to complete the test?

9. About what percent of the sophomores take between 51 and 63.3 minutes?

10. About what percent of the sophomores take less than 63.3 minutes to complete the test?

12-7 Practice

The Normal Distribution

Determine whether the data in each table appear to be *positively skewed*, *negatively skewed*, or *normally distributed*.

1.

Time Spent at a Museum Exhibit	
Minutes	Frequency
0–25	27
26–50	46
51–75	89
75–100	57
100+	24

2.

Average Age of High School Principals	
Age in Years	Number
31–35	3
36–40	8
41–45	15
46–50	32
51–55	40
56–60	38
60+	4

For Exercises 3 and 4, use the frequency table that shows the number of hours worked per week by 100 high school seniors.

Hours	Number of Students
0–8	30
9–17	45
18–25	20
26+	5

3. Make a histogram of the data.

4. Do the data appear to be *positively skewed*, *negatively skewed*, or *normally distributed*? Explain.

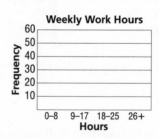

TESTING For Exercises 5–10, use the following information.

The scores on a test administered to prospective employees are normally distributed with a mean of 100 and a standard deviation of 15.

5. About what percent of the scores are between 70 and 130?

6. About what percent of the scores are between 85 and 130?

7. About what percent of the scores are over 115?

8. About what percent of the scores are lower than 85 or higher than 115?

9. If 80 people take the test, how many would you expect to score higher than 130?

10. If 75 people take the test, how many would you expect to score lower than 85?

11. TEMPERATURE The daily July surface temperature of a lake at a resort has a mean of 82° and a standard deviation of 4.2°. If you prefer to swim when the temperature is at least 77.8°, about what percent of the days does the temperature meet your preference?

12-7 Reading to Learn Mathematics

The Normal Distribution

Pre-Activity **How are the heights of professional athletes distributed?**

Read the introduction to Lesson 12-7 at the top of page 671 in your textbook.

There were 53 players on the team and the mean height was approximately 73.6. About what fraction of the players' heights are between 72 and 75, inclusive?

Reading the Lesson

1. Indicate whether each of the following statements is *true* or *false*.

   a. In a continuous probability distribution, there is a finite number of possible outcomes.

   b. Every normal distribution can be represented by a bell curve.

   c. A distribution that is represented by a curve that is high at the left and has a tail to the right is negatively skewed.

   d. A normal distribution is an example of a skewed distribution.

2. Ms. Rose gave the same quiz to her two geometry classes. She recorded the following scores.

   First-period class:

Score	0	1	2	3	4	5	6	7	8	9	10
Frequency	1	0	1	0	3	4	5	7	4	3	2

   Fifth-period class:

Score	0	1	2	3	4	5	6	7	8	9	10
Frequency	0	0	0	0	3	4	9	7	6	1	0

   In each class, 30 students took the quiz. The mean score for each class was 6.4. Which set of scores has the greater standard deviation? (Answer this question without doing any calculations.) Explain your answer.

Helping You Remember

3. Many students have trouble remembering how to determine if a curve represents a distribution that is *positively skewed* or *negatively skewed*. What is an easy way to remember this?

12-7 Enrichment

Street Networks: Finding All Possible Routes

A section of a city is laid out in square blocks. Going north from the intersection of First Avenue and First Street, the avenues are 1st, 2nd, 3rd, and so on. Going east, the streets are numbered in the same way.

Factorials can be used to find the number, $r(e, n)$, of different routes between two intersections. The formula is shown below.

$$r(e, n) = \frac{[(e - 1) + (n - 1)]!}{(e - 1)!(n - 1)!}$$

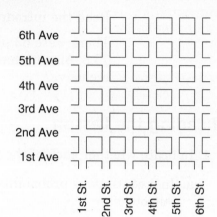

The number of streets going east is e; the number of avenues going north is n.

The following problems examine the possible routes from one location to another. Assume that you never use a route that is unnecessarily long. Assume that $e \geq 1$ and $n \geq 1$.

Solve each problem.

1. List all the possible routes from 1st Street and 1st Avenue to 4th Street and 3rd Avenue. Use ordered pairs to show the routes, with street numbers first, and avenue numbers second. For example, each route starts at (1, 1) and ends at (4, 3).

2. Use the formula to compute the number of routes from (1, 1) to (4, 3). There are 4 streets going east and 3 avenues going north.

3. Find the number of routes from 1st Street and 1st Avenue to 7th Street and 6th Avenue.

12-8 Study Guide and Intervention
Binomial Experiments

Binomial Expansions For situations with only 2 possible outcomes, you can use the Binomial Theorem to find probabilities. The coefficients of terms in a binomial expansion can be found by using combinations.

Example **What is the probability that 3 coins show heads and 3 show tails when 6 coins are tossed?**

There are 2 possible outcomes that are equally likely: heads (H) and tails (T). The tosses of 6 coins are independent events. When $(H + T)^6$ is expanded, the term containing H^3T^3, which represents 3 heads and 3 tails, is used to get the desired probability. By the Binomial Theorem the coefficient of H^3T^3 is $C(6, 3)$.

$P(3 \text{ heads, 3 tails}) = \dfrac{6!}{3!3!}\left(\dfrac{1}{2}\right)^3\left(\dfrac{1}{2}\right)^3$ $P(H) = \frac{1}{2}$ and $P(T) = \frac{1}{2}$

$= \dfrac{20}{64}$

$= \dfrac{5}{16}$

The probability of getting 3 heads and 3 tails is $\dfrac{5}{16}$ or 0.3125.

Exercises

Find each probability if a coin is tossed 8 times.

1. P(exactly 5 heads)

2. P(exactly 2 heads)

3. P(even number of heads)

4. P(at least 6 heads)

Mike guesses on all 10 questions of a true-false test. If the answers true and false are evenly distributed, find each probability.

5. Mike gets exactly 8 correct answers.

6. Mike gets at most 3 correct answers.

7. A die is tossed 4 times. What is the probability of tossing exactly two sixes?

Lesson 12-8

12-8 Study Guide and Intervention *(continued)*

Binomial Experiments

Binomial Experiments

	A binomial experiment is possible if and only if all of these conditions occur.
Binomial Experiments	• There are exactly two outcomes for each trial. • There is a fixed number of trials. • The trials are independent. • The probabilities for each trial are the same.

Example **Suppose a coin is weighted so that the probability of getting heads in any one toss is 90%. What is the probability of getting exactly 7 heads in 8 tosses?**

The probability of getting heads is $\frac{9}{10}$, and the probability of getting tails is $\frac{1}{10}$. There are $C(8, 7)$ ways to choose the 7 heads.

$$P(7 \text{ heads}) = C(8, 7)\left(\frac{9}{10}\right)^7\left(\frac{1}{10}\right)^1$$

$$= 8 \cdot \frac{9^7}{10^8}$$

$$\approx 0.38$$

The probability of getting 7 heads in 8 tosses is about 38%.

Exercises

1. **BASKETBALL** For any one foul shot, Derek has a probability of 0.72 of getting the shot in the basket. As part of a practice drill, he shoots 8 shots from the foul line.

   a. What is the probability that he gets in exactly 6 foul shots?

   b. What is the probability that he gets in at least 6 foul shots?

2. **SCHOOL** A teacher is trying to decide whether to have 4 or 5 choices per question on her multiple choice test. She wants to prevent students who just guess from scoring well on the test.

   a. On a 5-question multiple-choice test with 4 choices per question, what is the probability that a student can score at least 60% by guessing?

   b. What is the probability that a student can score at least 60% by guessing on a test of the same length with 5 choices per question?

3. Julie rolls two dice and adds the two numbers.

   a. What is the probability that the sum will be divisible by 3?

   b. If she rolls the dice 5 times what is the chance that she will get exactly 3 sums that are divisible by 3?

4. **SKATING** During practice a skater falls 15% of the time when practicing a triple axel. During one practice session he attempts 20 triple axels.

   a. What is the probability that he will fall only once?

   b. What is the probability that he will fall 4 times?

12-8 Skills Practice

Binomial Experiments

Find each probability if a coin is tossed 4 times.

1. P(4 heads)

2. P(0 heads)

3. P(exactly 3 heads)

4. P(exactly 2 heads)

5. P(exactly 1 head)

6. P(at least 3 heads)

Find each probability if a die is rolled 3 times.

7. P(exactly one 2)

8. P(exactly two 2s)

9. P(exactly three 2s)

10. P(at most one 2)

A town that presents a fireworks display during its July 4 celebration found the probability that a family with two or more children will watch the fireworks is $\frac{3}{5}$. If 5 of these families are selected at random, find each probability.

11. P(exactly 3 families watch the fireworks)

12. P(exactly 2 families watch the fireworks)

13. P(exactly 5 families watch the fireworks)

14. P(no families watch the fireworks)

15. P(at least 4 families watch the fireworks)

16. P(at most 1 family watches the fireworks)

One section of a standardized English language test has 10 true/false questions. Find each probability when a student guesses at all ten questions.

17. P(exactly 8 correct)

18. P(exactly 2 correct)

19. P(exactly half correct)

20. P(all 10 correct)

21. P(0 correct)

22. P(at least 8 correct)

12-8 Practice

Binomial Experiments

Find each probability if a coin is tossed 6 times.

1. P(exactly 3 tails)

2. P(exactly 5 tails)

3. P(0 tails)

4. P(at least 4 heads)

5. P(at least 4 tails)

6. P(at most 2 tails)

The probability of Chris making a free throw is $\frac{2}{3}$. If she shoots 5 times, find each probability.

7. P(all missed)

8. P(all made)

9. P(exactly 2 made)

10. P(exactly 1 missed)

11. P(at least 3 made)

12. P(at most 2 made)

When Tarin and Sam play a certain board game, the probability that Tarin will win a game is $\frac{3}{4}$. If they play 5 games, find each probability.

13. P(Sam wins only once)

14. P(Tarin wins exactly twice)

15. P(Sam wins exactly 3 games)

16. P(Sam wins at least 1 game)

17. P(Tarin wins at least 3 games)

18. P(Tarin wins at most 2 games)

19. SAFETY In August 2001, the American Automobile Association reported that 73% of Americans use seat belts. In a random selection of 10 Americans in 2001, what is the probability that exactly half of them use seat belts? **Source:** AAA

HEALTH For Exercises 20 and 21, use the following information.

In 2001, the American Heart Association reported that 50 percent of the Americans who receive heart transplants are ages 50–64 and 20 percent are ages 35–49. **Source:** American Heart Association

20. In a randomly selected group of 10 heart transplant recipients, what is the probability that at least 8 of them are ages 50–64?

21. In a randomly selected group of 5 heart transplant recipients, what is the probability that 2 of them are ages 35–49?

12-8 Reading to Learn Mathematics

Binomial Experiments

Pre-Activity **How can you determine whether guessing is worth it?**

Read the introduction to Lesson 12-8 at the top of page 676 in your textbook.

Suppose you are taking a 50-question multiple-choice test in which there are 5 answer choices for each question. You are told that no points will be deducted for wrong answers. Should you guess the answers to the questions you do not know? Explain your reasoning.

Reading the Lesson

1. Indicate whether each of the following is a *binomial experiment* or *not a binomial experiment*. If the experiment is not a binomial experiment, explain why.

   a. A fair coin is tossed 10 times and "heads" or "tails" is recorded each time.

   b. A pair of dice is thrown 5 times and the sum of the numbers that come up is recorded each time.

   c. There are 5 red marbles and 6 blue marbles in a bag. One marble is drawn from the bag and its color recorded. The marble is not put back in the bag. A second marble is drawn and its color recorded.

   d. There are 5 red marbles and 6 blue marbles in a bag. One marble is drawn from the bag and its color recorded. The marble is put back in the bag. A second marble is drawn and its color recorded.

2. Len randomly guesses the answers to all 6 multiple-choice questions on his chemistry test. Each question has 5 choices. Which of the following expressions gives the probability that he will get at least 4 of the answers correct?

   A. $P(6, 4)\left(\frac{1}{5}\right)^4\left(\frac{4}{5}\right)^2 + P(6, 5)\left(\frac{1}{5}\right)^5\left(\frac{4}{5}\right)^1 + P(6, 6)\left(\frac{1}{5}\right)^6\left(\frac{4}{5}\right)^0$

   B. $C(6, 4)\left(\frac{1}{5}\right)^4\left(\frac{4}{5}\right)^2 + C(6, 5)\left(\frac{1}{5}\right)^5\left(\frac{4}{5}\right)^1 + C(6, 6)\left(\frac{1}{5}\right)^6\left(\frac{4}{5}\right)^0$

   C. $C(6, 4)\left(\frac{1}{5}\right)^2\left(\frac{4}{5}\right)^4 + C(6, 5)\left(\frac{1}{5}\right)^1\left(\frac{4}{5}\right)^5 + C(6, 6)\left(\frac{1}{5}\right)^0\left(\frac{4}{5}\right)^6$

Helping You Remember

3. Some students have trouble remembering how to calculate binomial probabilities. What is an easy way to remember which numbers to put into an expression like $C(6, 4)\left(\frac{1}{5}\right)^2\left(\frac{4}{5}\right)^4$?

12-8 **Enrichment**

Misuses of Statistics

Statistics can be misleading. Graphs for a set of data can look very different
from one another. Compare the following graphs.

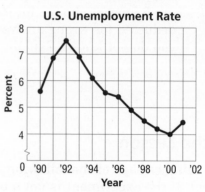

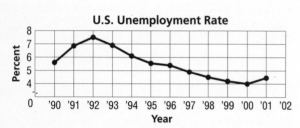

Source: U.S. Department of Labor   **Source:** U.S. Department of Labor

Notice that the two graphs show the same data, but the spacing in the
vertical and horizontal scales differs. Scales can be cramped or spread out to
make a graph that gives a certain impression. Which graph would you use to
give the impression that the unemployment rate dropped dramatically from
1990 to 2000?

Suppose that a car company claims, "75% of people surveyed say that our car
is better than the competition." If four people were asked which car they
preferred and 75% agreed, how many people thought that *Our Car* was
better?

The advertisement was misleading in other ways as well. For example, who
was surveyed—were the people company employees, or impartial buyers?

**Suppose an advertiser claims that 90% of all of one brand of car sold
in the last 10 years are still on the road.**

1. If 10,000 cars were sold, how many are still on the road?

2. If 1000 cars were sold, how many are still on the road?

3. Find an example to show how you think averages could be used in a
   misleading way.

4. A survey of a large sample of people who own small computers revealed
   that 85% of the people thought the instruction manuals should be better
   written. A manufacturer of small computers claimed that it surveyed
   many of the same people and found that all of them liked their manuals.
   Discuss the possible discrepancy in the results.

12-9 Study Guide and Intervention

Sampling and Error

Bias A sample of size n is random (or **unbiased**) when every possible sample of size n has an equal chance of being selected. If a sample is biased, then information obtained from it may not be reliable.

Example To find out how people in the U.S. feel about mass transit, people at a commuter train station are asked their opinion. Does this situation represent a random sample?

No; the sample includes only people who actually use a mass-transit facility. The sample does not include people who ride bikes, drive cars, or walk.

Exercises

Determine whether each situation would produce a random sample. Write *yes* or *no* and explain your answer.

1. asking people in Phoenix, Arizona, about rainfall to determine the average rainfall for the United States

2. obtaining the names of tree types in North America by surveying all of the U.S. National Forests

3. surveying every tenth person who enters the mall to find out about music preferences in that part of the country

4. interviewing country club members to determine the average number of televisions per household in the community

5. surveying all students whose ID numbers end in 4 about their grades and career counseling needs

6. surveying parents at a day care facility about their preferences for brands of baby food for a marketing campaign

7. asking people in a library about the number of magazines to which they subscribe in order to describe the reading habits of a town

Lesson 12-9

12-9 **Study Guide and Intervention** *(continued)*

Sampling and Error

Margin of Error The **margin of sampling error** gives a limit on the difference between how a sample responds and how the total population would respond.

Margin of Error	If the percent of people in a sample responding in a certain way is p and the size of the sample is n, then 95% of the time, the percent of the population responding in that same way will be between $p - ME$ and $p + ME$, where $ME = 2\sqrt{\dfrac{p(1-p)}{n}}$.

Example 1 In a survey of 4500 randomly selected voters, 62% favored candidate A. What is the margin of error?

$$ME = 2\sqrt{\frac{p(1-p)}{n}} \qquad \text{Formula for margin of sampling error}$$

$$= 2\sqrt{\frac{0.62 \cdot (1 - 0.62)}{4500}} \qquad p = 62\% \text{ or } 0.62,\ n = 4500$$

$$\approx 0.01447 \qquad \text{Use a calculator.}$$

The margin of error is about 1%. This means that there is a 95% chance that the percent of voters favoring candidate A is between $62 - 1$ or 61% and $62 + 1$ or 63%.

Example 2 The CD that 32% of teenagers surveyed plan to buy next is the latest from the popular new group BFA. If the margin of error of the survey is 2%, how many teenagers were surveyed?

$$ME = 2\sqrt{\frac{p(1-p)}{n}} \qquad \text{Formula for margin of sampling error}$$

$$0.02 = 2\sqrt{\frac{0.32 \cdot (1 - 0.32)}{n}} \qquad ME = 0.02,\ p = 0.32$$

$$0.01 = \sqrt{\frac{0.32(0.68)}{n}} \qquad \text{Divide each side by 2.}$$

$$0.0001 = \frac{0.32(0.68)}{n} \qquad \text{Square each side.}$$

$$n = \frac{0.32(0.68)}{0.0001} \qquad \text{Multiply by } n \text{ and divide by 0.0001}$$

$$n = 2176$$

2176 teenagers were surveyed.

Exercises

Find the margin of sampling error to the nearest percent.

1. $p = 45\%,\ n = 350$ **2.** $p = 12\%,\ n = 1500$ **3.** $p = 86\%,\ n = 600$

4. A study of 50,000 drivers in Indiana, Illinois, and Ohio showed that 68% preferred a speed limit of 75 mph over 65 mph on highways and country roads. What was the margin of sampling error to the nearest tenth of a percent?

12-9 Skills Practice

Sampling and Error

Determine whether each situation would produce a random sample. Write *yes* or *no* and explain your answer.

1. calling households at 3:30 P.M. on Tuesday to determine a political candidate's support

2. polling customers as they exit a sporting goods store about their attitudes about exercise

3. recording the number of sit-ups performed by 15-year old girls in the high schools of a large school district to determine the fitness of all high-school girls in the district

4. selecting two of a city's 20 apartment buildings for a survey to determine the desire of apartment dwellers in the city to own a home

5. In a large school district, the superintendent of schools interviews two teachers at random from each school to determine whether teachers in the district think students are assigned too much or too little homework.

6. For seven consecutive days, one hour each in the morning, afternoon, and evening, every tenth customer who enters a mall is asked to choose her or his favorite store.

Find the margin of sampling error to the nearest percent.

7. $p = 85\%, n = 100$

8. $p = 78\%, n = 100$

9. $p = 15\%, n = 100$

10. $p = 37\%, n = 500$

11. $p = 12\%, n = 500$

12. $p = 93\%, n = 500$

13. $p = 23\%, n = 1000$

14. $p = 56\%, n = 1000$

15. **HEALTH** In a recent poll of cigarette smokers, 67% of those surveyed said they had tried to quit smoking within the last year. The margin of error was 3%. About how many people were surveyed?

Lesson 12-9

12-9 Practice

Sampling and Error

Determine whether each situation would produce a random sample. Write *yes* or *no* and explain your answer.

1. calling every twentieth registered voter to determine whether people own or rent their homes in your community

2. predicting local election results by polling people in every twentieth residence in all the different neighborhoods of your community

3. to find out why not many students are using the library, a school's librarian gives a questionnaire to every tenth student entering the library

4. testing overall performance of tires on interstate highways only

5. selecting every 50th hamburger from a fast-food restaurant chain and determining its fat content to assess the fat content of hamburgers served in fast-food restaurant chains throughout the country

6. assigning all shift workers in a manufacturing plant a unique identification number, and then placing the numbers in a hat and drawing 30 at random to determine the annual average salary of the workers

Find the margin of sampling error to the nearest percent.

7. $p = 26\%, n = 100$ 8. $p = 55\%, n = 100$ 9. $p = 75\%, n = 500$

10. $p = 14\%, n = 500$ 11. $p = 96\%, n = 1000$ 12. $p = 21\%, n = 1000$

13. $p = 34\%, n = 1000$ 14. $p = 49\%, n = 1500$ 15. $p = 65\%, n = 1500$

16. **COMPUTING** According to a poll of 500 teenagers, 43% said that they use a personal computer at home. What is the margin of sampling error?

17. **TRUST** A survey of 605 people, ages 13–33, shows that 68% trust their parents more than their best friends to tell them the truth. What is the margin of sampling error?

18. **PRODUCTIVITY** A study by the University of Illinois in 1995 showed an increase in productivity by 10% of the employees who wore headsets and listened to music of their choice while they were working. The margin of sampling error for the study was about 7%. How many employees participated in the study?

12-9 Reading to Learn Mathematics

Sampling and Error

Pre-Activity **How are opinion polls used in political campaigns?**

Read the introduction to Lesson 12-9 at the top of page 682 in your textbook.

Do you think the results of the survey about the presidential preferences demonstrates that Bush was actually ahead in Florida a month before the election? If there is not enough information given to determine this, list at least two questions you would ask about the survey that would help you determine the significance of the survey.

Reading the Lesson

1. Determine whether each situation would produce a random sample. Write *yes* or *no* and explain your answer.

   a. asking all the customers at five restaurants on the same evening how many times a month they eat dinner in restaurants to determine how often the average American eats dinner in a restaurants

   b. putting the names of all seniors at your high school in a hat and then drawing 20 names for a survey to find out where seniors would like to hold their prom

2. A survey determined that 58% of registered voters in the United States support increased federal spending for education. The margin of error for this survey is 4%. Explain in your own words what this tells you about the actual percentage of registered voters who support increased spending for education.

Helping You Remember

3. The formula for margin of sampling error may be tricky to remember. A good way to start is to think about the variables that must be included in the formula. What are these variables, and what do they represent? What is an easy way to remember which variable goes in the denominator in the formula?

Lesson 12-9

12-9 Enrichment

Shapes of Distribution Curves

Graphs of frequency distributions can be described as either symmetric or skewed.

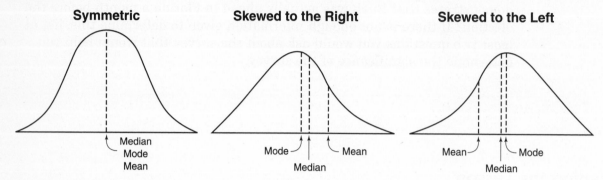

Symmetric   **Skewed to the Right**   **Skewed to the Left**

In a distribution skewed to the right, there are a larger number of high values. The long "tail" extends to the right.

In a distribution skewed to the left, there are a larger number of low values. The "tail" extends to the left.

For each of the following, state whether the distribution is symmetric or skewed. If it is skewed, tell whether it is skewed to the right or to the left.

1.   2.   3.

4.   5.   6.

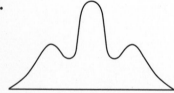      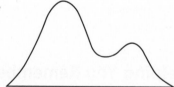

A vertical line above the median divides the area under a frequency curve in half.

7. Where is the median in a symmetric distribution?

8. Where is the median in a skewed distribution?

Glencoe Algebra 2

12 # Chapter 12 Test, Form 1

Write the letter for the correct answer in the blank at the right of each question.

1. Carl purchased four new shirts and three new pairs of pants. How many new outfits can he make with these items?

   A. 12   **B.** 7   **C.** 9   **D.** 81

   1. _____

2. **TRIATHALON** During training, a triathlete works on biking, swimming, and running times. How many ways can a triathlete choose the order of these activities in a training session?

   A. 4   **B.** 9   **C.** 5   **D.** 6

   2. _____

3. Evaluate $P(7, 2)$.

   A. 49   **B.** 21   **C.** 42   **D.** 14

   3. _____

4. Evaluate $C(6, 2)$.

   A. 30   **B.** 15   **C.** 12   **D.** 36

   4. _____

5. Find the odds of an event occurring, given that the probability of the event is $\frac{3}{11}$.

   A. 3:11   **B.** 8:3   **C.** 8:11   **D.** 3:8

   5. _____

6. The table and relative-frequency histogram show the distribution of the number of tails when 2 coins are tossed. Find $P(T = 2 \text{ tails})$.

   A. $\frac{1}{4}$ **B.** $\frac{1}{2}$

   C. 1   **D.** 0

T = Tails	0	1	2
Probability	$\frac{1}{4}$	$\frac{1}{2}$	$\frac{1}{4}$

   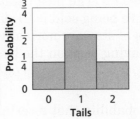

   6. _____

7. A blue die and a red die are tossed. What is the probability that a 6 will appear on both dice?

   A. $\frac{1}{18}$ **B.** $\frac{1}{36}$ **C.** $\frac{1}{2}$ **D.** $\frac{1}{11}$

   7. _____

8. A jar contains 10 purple marbles and 2 red marbles. If two marbles are chosen at random with no replacement, what is the probability that 2 purple marbles are chosen?

   A. $\frac{25}{36}$ **B.** $\frac{5}{6}$ **C.** $\frac{15}{22}$ **D.** $\frac{1}{5}$

   8. _____

9. A bag contains 6 cherry, 8 strawberry, and 9 grape-flavored candies. What is the probability of selecting a cherry or a grape flavored candy?

   A. $\frac{15}{23}$ **B.** $\frac{14}{23}$ **C.** $\frac{17}{23}$ **D.** $\frac{54}{529}$

   9. _____

10. A die is rolled. What is the probability of rolling a 6 or a number greater than 4?

    A. $\frac{2}{3}$ **B.** $\frac{1}{2}$ **C.** $\frac{1}{6}$ **D.** $\frac{1}{3}$

    10. _____

11. A coin is tossed 5 times. Find $P(5 \text{ tails})$.

    A. $\frac{1}{5}$ **B.** $\frac{1}{10}$ **C.** $\frac{1}{16}$ **D.** $\frac{1}{32}$

    11. _____

Assessment

12. Which measure of central tendency best represents a data set with outliers?
    A. mode   B. mean   C. median   D. variance   12. _____

For Questions 13–15, use the data set {10, 12, 12, 14, 22}.

13. Find the mean.
    A. 17.5   B. 14   C. 70   D. 13   13. _____

14. Find the variance. Round to the nearest tenth, if necessary.
    A. 17.6   B. 88   C. 4.2   D. 4   14. _____

15. Find the standard deviation. Round to the nearest tenth, if necessary.
    A. 17.6   B. 14.6   C. 4.2   D. 14   15. _____

16. Classify the data in the table.
    A. positively skewed
    B. negatively skewed
    C. normally distributed
    D. discrete distribution

Amount Spent on Lunch	
Less than $4.00	18%
$4.00–$7.99	47%
$8.00–$11.99	16%
$12.00–$15.99	11%
$16.00 or more	8%

16. _____

17. **CAR SALES** The mean stay of a car on a lot before being sold is 21 days, with a standard deviation of 3 days. The lengths of stay are normally distributed. What percent of the cars are sold after having been on the lot between 18 and 24 days?
    A. 95%   B. 34%   C. 68%   D. 5%   17. _____

18. The probability that a certain team will win a baseball game is $\frac{1}{3}$. In a 5-game series, what is the probability that the team will win all five games?
    A. $\frac{1}{15}$ B. $\frac{1}{243}$ C. $\frac{1}{3}$ D. $\frac{5}{243}$ 18. _____

19. **COMMUTERS** Which group should be surveyed to determine how people commute to work in order to produce a random sample?
    A. students in your school
    B. people passing through a toll booth on a given day
    C. people in your state whose last name begins with S
    D. people whose annual income is greater than $1,000,000   19. _____

20. Find the margin of sampling error when $p = 45\%$ and $n = 100$ if
    $ME = 2\sqrt{\dfrac{p(1-p)}{n}}$.
    A. 9%   B. 10%   C. 5%   D. 1%   20. _____

Bonus If f represents the probability of rolling a 5 and n represents the probability of rolling any other number, which term of $(f + n)^4 = f^4 + 4f^3n + 6f^2n^2 + 4fn^3 + n^4$ represents the probability of rolling exactly three 5s in 4 rolls of a die? Find the probability.   B: _____

12 Chapter 12 Test, Form 2A

Write the letter for the correct answer in the blank at the right of each question.

1. **LICENSE PLATES** A license plate has one letter (not I or O) followed by five digits. How many different plates are possible?

   A. 1200   **B.** 2,400,000   **C.** 725,760   **D.** 100,000   1. _____

2. How many 3-letter identification codes are possible if no letter is repeated?

   A. 17,576   **B.** 2600   **C.** 78   **D.** 15,600   2. _____

3. Evaluate $P(10, 4)$.

   A. 5040   **B.** 151,200   **C.** 30,240   **D.** 210   3. _____

4. A group has 6 men and 5 women. How many ways can a committee of 3 men and 2 women be formed?

   A. 200   **B.** 150   **C.** 7200   **D.** 2400   4. _____

5. The odds that an event will occur are 7:2. What is the probability that the event will occur?

   A. $\dfrac{9}{14}$ **B.** $\dfrac{7}{9}$ **C.** $\dfrac{2}{9}$ **D.** $\dfrac{2}{7}$ 5. _____

6. Two marbles are chosen at random from a bag containing 3 blue and 2 red marbles. The relative-frequency histogram shows the distribution of the number of red marbles chosen. Find $P(2\text{ red})$.

   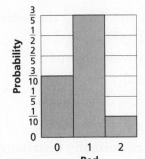

   A. $\dfrac{1}{10}$ **B.** $\dfrac{1}{5}$

   C. $\dfrac{3}{5}$ **D.** $\dfrac{3}{10}$ 6. _____

7. A red die and a blue die are tossed. What is the probability that the red die shows a 5 and the blue die shows an even number?

   A. $\dfrac{1}{36}$ **B.** $\dfrac{1}{18}$ **C.** $\dfrac{1}{12}$ **D.** $\dfrac{2}{3}$ 7. _____

8. Tickets are numbered 1 to 50 and are placed in a box. Three tickets are drawn at random without replacement. What is the probability that the numbers are all greater than 35?

   A. $\dfrac{27}{1000}$ **B.** $\dfrac{13}{560}$ **C.** $\dfrac{3}{10}$ **D.** $\dfrac{1}{7840}$ 8. _____

9. From 4 yellow and 9 blue marbles, 3 are selected. What is the probability that all 3 are yellow or all 3 are blue?

   A. $\dfrac{4}{143}$ **B.** $\dfrac{4}{13}$ **C.** $\dfrac{42}{143}$ **D.** $\dfrac{84}{143}$ 9. _____

10. A card is drawn from a deck of cards. What is the probability of drawing a club or a face card? (*Hint*: A face card is a jack, queen, or king.)

    A. $\dfrac{25}{52}$ **B.** $\dfrac{3}{13}$ **C.** $\dfrac{11}{26}$ **D.** $\dfrac{7}{13}$ 10. _____

11. A coin is tossed 5 times. Find $P(\text{at least 3 tails})$.

    A. $\dfrac{3}{16}$ **B.** $\dfrac{1}{2}$ **C.** $\dfrac{5}{16}$ **D.** $\dfrac{3}{5}$ 11. _____

Assessment

12. How many different arrangements of the letters of the word *radar* are possible?

    A. 120   **B.** 60   **C.** 30   **D.** 480   12. _____

TEMPERATURES For Questions 13–15, use the data in the table. Round to the nearest tenth, if necessary.

Record Low Temperatures in Honolulu, HI (°F)											
Jan	Feb	Mar	Apr	May	Jun	Jul	Aug	Sep	Oct	Nov	Dec
52	53	55	56	60	65	66	67	66	61	57	54

Source: www.weather.com

13. Which measure of central tendency is *not* a good representation of the data?

    A. mean   **B.** mode   **C.** median   **D.** middle   13. _____

14. Find the variance of the temperatures.

    A. 28.4   **B.** 5.3   **C.** 59.3   **D.** 340.7   14. _____

15. Find the standard deviation of the temperatures.

    A. 52°F   **B.** 5.3°F   **C.** 5.6°F   **D.** 28.4°F   15. _____

16. Classify the data in the table.

    A. positively skewed

    B. negatively skewed

    C. normally distributed

    D. discrete distribution

Age of Population of Iowa in 2000	
Age	Number of People
0–24	978,875
25–44	795,499
45–64	644,861
65–84	357,074
Over 84	45,848

16. _____

17. POTTERY The diameters of pottery bowls are normally distributed. The mean of the diameters is 22 cm and the standard deviation is 2 cm. What percent of the bowls have diameters between 18 and 26 cm?

    A. 13.5%   **B.** 34%   **C.** 68%   **D.** 95%   17. _____

18. In a local car lot, $\frac{1}{6}$ of the cars have standard transmissions. Find the probability that 3 of 4 randomly-selected cars have standard transmissions.

    A. $\frac{125}{324}$ **B.** $\frac{5}{9}$ **C.** $\frac{5}{324}$ **D.** $\frac{5}{1296}$ 18. _____

19. A school librarian wants to determine the reading interests of students. A survey of which group would produce a random sample?

    A. every third student leaving the library on a given day

    B. students on the football team

    C. every fifth person entering the school in the morning

    D. seniors planning to attend college   19. _____

20. HOMEWORK In a survey of 320 students, 32% spent at least 1 hour per night on homework. Find the margin of sampling error.

    A. 5%   **B.** 21%   **C.** 3%   **D.** 10%   20. _____

Bonus Write a data set having 7 values that has a median of 24 and a mean of 20.

                                                    B: _____

12 **Chapter 12 Test, Form 2B**

Write the letter for the correct answer in the blank at the right of each question.

1. An ice cream store has 31 flavors of ice cream and 10 toppings. A regular sundae has one flavor of ice cream, one topping, and comes with or without whipped cream. How many different ice cream sundaes can be ordered?

   A. 310   **B.** 372   **C.** 620   **D.** 82   1. _____

2. How many 5-digit codes are possible if 0 cannot be used and no digit can be repeated?

   A. 15,120   **B.** 45   **C.** 30,240   **D.** 59,049   2. _____

3. A clown has 7 balloons, each a different color. There are 5 children. How many ways can the clown give each child a balloon?

   A. 21   **B.** 5040   **C.** 42   **D.** 2520   3. _____

4. Evaluate $C(13, 9)$.

   A. 17,160   **B.** 715   **C.** 259,459,200   **D.** 117   4. _____

5. The probability that an event will occur is $\frac{11}{15}$. What are the odds that the event will occur?

   A. 15:11   **B.** 11:15   **C.** 4:11   **D.** 11:4   5. _____

6. Two marbles are chosen at random from a bag containing 3 blue and 2 red marbles. The relative-frequency histogram shows the distribution of the number of red marbles chosen. Find $P(0 \text{ red})$.

   A. 0   **B.** $\frac{8}{15}$ **C.** $\frac{3}{10}$ **D.** $\frac{2}{5}$

   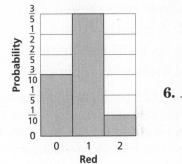

   6. _____

7. A red die and a blue die are tossed. What is the probability that the red die shows a 3 and the blue die shows a number greater than 3?

   A. $\frac{1}{10}$ **B.** $\frac{1}{5}$ **C.** $\frac{1}{12}$ **D.** $\frac{3}{5}$ 7. _____

8. Tickets are numbered 1 to 50 and placed in a box. Three tickets are drawn at random without replacement. What is the probability that their numbers are all greater than 25?

   A. $\frac{1}{8}$ **B.** $\frac{23}{196}$ **C.** $\frac{69}{625}$ **D.** $\frac{1}{2}$ 8. _____

9. From 4 yellow and 8 blue marbles, 3 are selected. What is the probability that all three are yellow or all three are blue?

   A. $\frac{3}{11}$ **B.** $\frac{1}{55}$ **C.** $\frac{14}{55}$ **D.** $\frac{3}{220}$ 9. _____

10. A card is drawn from a standard deck of cards. What is $P(\text{heart or a 6})$?

    A. $\frac{9}{26}$ **B.** $\frac{17}{52}$ **C.** $\frac{1}{4}$ **D.** $\frac{4}{13}$ 10. _____

11. A coin is tossed 5 times. Find $P(\text{at most 4 tails})$.

    A. $\frac{3}{16}$ **B.** $\frac{13}{16}$ **C.** $\frac{1}{32}$ **D.** $\frac{31}{32}$ 11. _____

Assessment

12. How many different arrangements of the letters of the word *doodle* are possible?

   A. 180   **B.** 720   **C.** 15   **D.** 90   12. _____

TEMPERATURES For Questions 13–15, use the data in the table. Round to the nearest tenth, if necessary.

Record High Temperatures in Anchorage, Alaska (°F)											
Jan	Feb	Mar	Apr	May	Jun	Jul	Aug	Sep	Oct	Nov	Dec
50	48	51	65	77	85	82	82	73	61	53	48

Source: www.weather.com

13. Which measure of central tendency is *not* a good representation of the data?

   A. middle   **B.** median   **C.** mode   **D.** mean   13. _____

14. Find the variance of the temperatures.

   A. 4366.2   **B.** 64.6   **C.** 2342.9   **D.** 195.2   14. _____

15. Find the standard deviation of the temperatures.

   A. 14.6°F   **B.** 14.0°F   **C.** 63.0°F   **D.** 64.6°F   15. _____

16. Classify the data in the table.

   A. positively skewed

   B. negatively skewed

   C. normally distributed

   D. discrete distribution

Age of Population of Rhode Island in 2000	
Age	Number of People
0–14	206,423
15–34	265,778
35–54	308,946
55–74	159,092
over 74	69,264

Source: Census 2000

16. _____

17. For 2000 patients, blood-clotting time was normally distributed with a mean of 8 seconds and a standard deviation of 3 seconds. What percent had blood-clotting times between 5 and 11 seconds?

   A. 68%   **B.** 34%   **C.** 49.5%   **D.** 47.5%   17. _____

18. During a sale, $\frac{1}{6}$ of the CD prices are reduced. Find the probability that 2 of 4 randomly-selected CDs have reduced prices.

   A. $\frac{5}{36}$ **B.** $\frac{25}{1296}$ **C.** $\frac{25}{216}$ **D.** $\frac{5}{216}$ 18. _____

19. A music teacher wants to determine the music preferences of students. A survey of which group would produce a random sample?

   A. students in the school band

   B. students attending the annual jazz concert

   C. students in every odd-numbered homeroom

   D. every other player on the baseball roster   19. _____

20. ELECTIONS In an election poll, 56% of 400 voters chose a certain candidate. Find the margin of sampling error.

   A. 5%   **B.** 2%   **C.** 4%   **D.** 7%   20. _____

Bonus Write a data set having 7 data values that has a median of 20 and a mean of 24.   **B:** _____

                                       Glencoe Algebra 2

12 Chapter 12 Test, Form 2C

SCORE _____

1. **BELTS** A clothing store sells belts in 3 colors, 4 designs, and 6 sizes. How many different belts are available?

1. _____

2. Five children stand in a line to play a game. How many different ways can the children be arranged?

2. _____

3. **CROSS-COUNTRY** Twelve runners are in a cross-country race. How many different ways can they finish first, second, and third?

3. _____

4. Five cheerleaders will be chosen from a group of 15 students. How many different cheerleading squads can be formed?

4. _____

5. The odds of an event occurring are 4 to 7. What is the probability that the event will occur?

5. _____

6. Two socks are chosen at random from a drawer containing 6 black and 3 blue socks. The table and relative-frequency histogram show the distribution of the number of black socks chosen. Find $P(B = 2)$.

B = Black	0	1	2
Probability	$\frac{1}{12}$	$\frac{1}{2}$	$\frac{5}{12}$

6. _____

7. A die is rolled three times. What is P(no 5s)?

7. _____

8. Two cards are drawn from a standard deck of 52 cards without replacement. Find the probability that the first card is an ace and the second is a 2.

8. _____

9. From a group of 6 men and 8 women, a committee of 3 is selected. Find the probability that all 3 are men or all 3 are women.

9. _____

10. Each of the numbers 1 to 25 is written on a card and placed in a bag. If one card is drawn at random, what is the probability that it is a multiple of 4 or a multiple of 5?

10. _____

11. Seven coins are tossed. Find P(at least 6 tails).

11. _____

12. If the probability of rain in a certain city is $\frac{1}{8}$ on any given day, find the probability that rain will fall on exactly one day of a three-day visit to the city.

12. _____

13. How many different arrangements of the letters in the word ILLINOIS are possible?

13. _____

Assessment

12 Chapter 12 Test, Form 2C *(continued)*

TEMPERATURES For Questions 14–16, use the data in the table. Round to the nearest tenth, if necessary.

Record High Temperatures in Memphis, TN (°F)											
Jan	Feb	Mar	Apr	May	Jun	Jul	Aug	Sep	Oct	Nov	Dec
78	81	85	94	99	104	108	105	103	95	85	81

Source: www.weather.com

14. If you were a member of the Chamber of Commerce, which measure of central tendency would you use to convince someone that Memphis has a comfortable climate? Explain.

14. _____

15. Find the variance of the temperatures.

15. _____

16. Find the standard deviation of the temperatures.

16. _____

17. **EDUCATION** Determine whether the data in the table is *positively skewed, negatively skewed,* or *normally distributed.*

17. _____

Educational Attainment in Georgia for persons over 25 years of age, as of 2000	
Less than 9th grade	484,000
9th to 12th grade, no diploma	686,000
High school graduate	1,193,000
Some college or associate degree	884,000
Bachelor's degree	520,000
Graduate or professional degree	258,000

Source: www.census.gov

18. **COLLEGE ENTRANCE EXAM** The scores on a standardized college entrance examination are found to be normally distributed. The mean is 85 and the standard deviation is 11. What percent scored between 85 and 107?

18. _____

19. Determine whether the situation would produce a random sample and explain your answer: *surveying your class to determine the most-admired person in the United States by people your age.*

19. _____

20. In a sample of 120 small business owners, 64% said they preferred a certain company for office supplies. Find the margin of sampling error.

20. _____

Bonus Student test grades were normally distributed, and grades between 62 and 86 were within three standard deviations of the mean. Find the mean and standard deviation of the set of grades.

B: _____

Glencoe Algebra 2

12   **Chapter 12 Test, Form 2D**

1. A store sells T-shirts in 7 colors, 5 designs, and 3 sizes. How many different T-shirts are available?

     1. _____

2. Marva needs to mow the lawn, pay her bills, walk the dog, and return a phone call. How many ways can she choose to order her tasks?

     2. _____

3. How many different arrangements of three coins can be made if you have a penny, a nickel, a dime, a quarter, and a silver dollar?

     3. _____

4. How many different 5-player basketball teams can be formed from a group of 12 people?

     4. _____

5. If the probability that an event will occur is $\frac{5}{12}$, what are the odds that it will occur?

     5. _____

6. Two socks are chosen at random from a drawer containing 4 black and 3 blue socks. The table and relative-frequency histogram show the distribution of the number of blue socks chosen. Find $P(B = 1)$.

     6. _____

B = Blue	0	1	2
Probability	$\frac{2}{7}$	$\frac{4}{7}$	$\frac{1}{7}$

7. A die is rolled three times. What is P(three 5s)?

     7. _____

8. Two cards are drawn from a standard deck of 52 cards without replacement. Find the probability that both cards are aces.

     8. _____

9. From a group of 7 men and 5 women, a 4-person committee is chosen. What is the probability that all 4 are men or all 4 are women?

     9. _____

10. Each of the numbers 1 to 20 is written on a card and placed in a bag. If one card is drawn at random, what is the probability that it is a multiple of 3 or a multiple of 5?

     10. _____

11. Eight coins are tossed. Find P(at least 7 heads).

     11. _____

12. If the probability of rain in a certain city is $\frac{2}{5}$ on any given day, find the probability that rain will fall on exactly one day of a three-day visit to the city.

     12. _____

Glencoe Algebra 2

12 **Chapter 12 Test, Form 2D** *(continued)*

13. How many different arrangements of the letters in the word INDIANA are possible?

13. _____

14. The sales prices of several cars on a used car lot are $18,900; $20,500; $29,900; $19,800; and $21,750. Which measure of central tendency best represents the data? Explain.

14. _____

For Questions 15 and 16, use the data in the table that shows average precipitation in Grand Junction, Colorado. Round to the nearest hundredth, if necessary.

Average Precipitation in Grand Junction, CO (in.)											
Jan	Feb	Mar	Apr	May	Jun	Jul	Aug	Sep	Oct	Nov	Dec
0.6	0.5	0.9	0.8	0.9	0.5	0.7	0.8	0.8	1.0	0.7	0.6

Source: www.weather.com

15. Find the variance of the data.

15. _____

16. Find the standard deviation of the data.

16. _____

17. Determine whether the data in the table is *positively skewed, negatively skewed,* or *normally distributed.*

17. _____

Age of Population of Florida in 2000	
Age	**Number of People**
0–24	4,870,160
25–44	4,442,638
45–64	3,581,676
65–84	2,449,573
Over 84	269,388

Source: Census 2000

18. COLLEGE ENTRANCE EXAM The scores on a standardized college entrance examination are found to be normally distributed. The mean is 78 and the standard deviation is 13. What percent scored between 52 and 78?

18. _____

19. Determine whether the situation would produce a random sample and explain your answer: *surveying persons with library cards to determine if a city should raise taxes to pay for a new library.*

19. _____

20. In a survey of 60 customers in a supermarket, 40% expect to use the express line. What is the margin of sampling error?

20. _____

Bonus Student test grades were normally distributed, and grades between 68 and 86 were within three standard deviations of the mean. Find the mean and standard deviation of the set of grades.

B: _____

12 **Chapter 12 Test, Form 3**

1. Each day, Jonathan chooses one of six routes to work. How many different ways can Jonathan get to work over a five-day period?

1. _____

2. How many different ways can 9 entertainers appear on an awards show if the guest of honor must appear first or last?

2. _____

3. How many ways can you select 4 pizza toppings from a total of 8 toppings? Is this a permutation or a combination? Explain.

3. _____

4. Evaluate $C(13, 5) \cdot C(9, 4)$.

4. _____

5. A coin purse contains 4 pennies, 5 nickels, and 8 dimes. Three coins are selected at random. Find the probability of selecting one coin of each type.

5. _____

6. Three students are selected at random from a group of 4 males and 6 females. The table and relative-frequency histogram show the distribution of the number of males chosen. Find P(two females).

6. _____

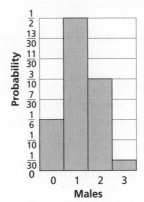

M = Male	0	1	2	3
Probability	$\frac{1}{6}$	$\frac{1}{2}$	$\frac{3}{10}$	$\frac{1}{30}$

7. A die is rolled four times. Find P(four of the same number).

7. _____

8. Four cards are drawn from a standard deck of 52 cards without replacement. Find the probability that the first card is a heart, the second is a club, and the third and fourth are diamonds.

8. _____

9. From a group of 8 men and 10 women, a committee of 5 is to be selected at random. Find P(at least 3 men).

9. _____

10. Two cards are drawn from a standard deck of cards. Find P(both black or both 9s).

10. _____

11. How many ways can 4 basketball shoes, 2 tennis shoes, and 5 running shoes be arranged on a shelf if the shoes are grouped according to type?

11. _____

Assessment

12 | **Chapter 12 Test, Form 3** *(continued)*

TAXES For Questions 12–15, use the data in the table that shows the per capita taxes, in dollars, in the 10 states listed. Round to the nearest cent, if necessary.

State	Taxes	State	Taxes
Arizona	1489	Iowa	1678
California	2073	Maine	1905
Colorado	1483	Maryland	1790
Delaware	2665	Michigan	2161
Illinois	1641	Missouri	1512

Source: *World Almanac*

12. Which measure of central tendency might a realtor in Maryland use to convince a client that the per capita taxes were reasonable? Explain.

12. _____

13. Find the variance of the taxes.

13. _____

14. Find the standard deviation of the taxes.

14. _____

15. Determine whether the data in the table is *positively skewed, negatively skewed,* or *normally distributed.*

15. _____

16. **IQ TESTS** Scores on an IQ test are normally distributed. The mean is 100 and the standard deviation is 15. If 6000 people took the test, how many of them scored between 85 and 130?

16. _____

17. Find P(at least four 4s) if a die is rolled 6 times.

17. _____

18. In a certain city in June, the probability that the temperature will rise above 80°F is 0.7. For the first 8 days, what is P(temperature will rise above 80°F exactly 3 times)? Round to the nearest hundredth.

18. _____

19. Determine whether the situation would produce a random sample and explain your answer: *surveying town residents whose license number ends in 5 to determine whether to increase taxes to pay for road repair.*

19. _____

20. **PETS** In a survey of pet owners, 68% preferred dogs to any other kind of pet. The margin of sampling error was 5%. How many people were surveyed?

20. _____

Bonus 20% of the students in a high school were surveyed to determine their favorite pizza topping. If 43% of those surveyed responded "pepperoni," and the margin of sampling error was 6.2%, how many students attend the high school?

B: _____

Glencoe Algebra 2

12 **Chapter 12 Open-Ended Assessment**   SCORE _____

Demonstrate your knowledge by giving a clear, concise solution to each problem. Be sure to include all relevant drawings and justify your answers. You may show your solutions in more than one way or investigate beyond the requirements of the problem.

1. Kathy, Alma, and Steven are working on a group quiz. One question is as follows.

   Two dice are rolled. Find the probability that the first die is a 5 or a 6, and the second die is an even number.

   All three students agree to let A represent rolling a 5 or a 6, and B represent rolling an even number. But Kathy argues that the solution is $P(A) + P(B) = \frac{2}{6} + \frac{3}{6} = \frac{5}{6}$, Alma feels certain that the solution should be $P(A) \cdot P(B) = \frac{2}{6} \cdot \frac{3}{6} = \frac{6}{36} = \frac{1}{6}$, and Steven is convinced that the correct solution is $P(A) + P(B) - P(A \text{ and } B) = \frac{2}{6} + \frac{3}{6} - \frac{1}{6} = \frac{4}{6} - \frac{2}{3}$.

   a. Which student, if any, is correct? Explain your reasoning.

   b. For one of the incorrect solutions above, write a probability problem for which that solution would be correct.

2. **a.** One day, your math teacher, Mr. Butler, looks at your exam scores and informs you that your score distribution is negatively skewed. How do you feel about this news? Explain your reasoning.

   b. The next day, Mr. Butler announces that the class scores on the last exam were normally distributed, that scores between 56 and 98 fell within three standard deviations of the mean, and that students whose scores fell within one standard deviation of the mean would earn a grade of C on the exam. Explain how to estimate the mean score, the standard deviation of the class scores, and the range of grades for which a student would earn a grade of C. Determine the indicated values.

3. Greg and Jacqui are planning a dinner party for 6 guests. After dinner, they plan to separate into two teams to play charades.

   a. Explain how you could determine the number of different possible arrangements of guests and hosts into two teams. Include in your explanation whether the formula $P(n, r) = \frac{n!}{(n - r)!}$ or the formula $C(n, r) = \frac{n!}{(n - r)!r!}$ would be helpful in determining the number of arrangements. Explain your reasoning and determine the number of arrangements that are possible.

   b. Would the number of possible arrangements change if Greg and Jacqui decided that they should be on different teams? If so, how many arrangements would be possible under those conditions? Explain your reasoning.

Assessment

12 Chapter 12 Vocabulary Test/Review

area diagram	failure	mutually exclusive events	relative-frequency
binomial experiment	Fundamental Counting	normal distribution	histogram
combination	Principle	odds	sample space
compound event	inclusive events	outcome	simple event
continuous probability	independent events	permutation	skewed distribution
distribution	linear permutation	probability	standard deviation
dependent events	margin of sampling error	probability distribution	success
discrete probability	measure of central	random	unbiased sample
distributions	tendency	random variable	variance
event	measure of variation		

Write whether each sentence is *true* or *false*. If false, replace the underlined word or words to make a true sentence.

1. A selection of objects in which order is not important is called a <u>permutation</u>.

1. _____

2. The graph of a <u>normal distribution</u> is a bell curve.

2. _____

3. Range, variance, and <u>odds</u> are measures of the spread of a set of data.

3. _____

4. Probability distributions with a finite number of possible values are called <u>continuous probability distributions</u>.

4. _____

5. Tossing a coin ten times is an example of a <u>linear permutation</u>.

5. _____

6. A relative-frequency distribution is a graph of a <u>probability distribution</u>.

6. _____

7. Two or more choices for which the result of one choice does not affect the result of another are called <u>independent events</u>.

7. _____

8. Events that consist of two or more simple events are called <u>dependent events</u>.

8. _____

9. The mean, the median, and the mode are <u>measures of variation</u>.

9. _____

10. A curve or histogram that is not symmetric represents a(n) <u>unbiased sample</u>.

10. _____

In your own words—
Define each term.

11. mutually exclusive events

12. random sample

12 Chapter 12 Quiz
(Lessons 12–1 through 12–3)

1. **Standardized Test Practice** Lisa selects a car from 4 models. Each model comes in 5 colors. How many different ways can she select a car?

   A. 24   **B.** 16   **C.** 9   **D.** 20

   1. _____

2. How many four-digit codes are possible if no digit may be used more than once?

   2. _____

3. A group of 3 women and 1 man is chosen from 7 women and 5 men. Does this involve a *permutation* or a *combination*? Find the number of different groups that can be formed.

   3. _____

4. Cards are numbered 1 through 20. Find the probability that a card drawn at random will contain a number greater than 11. Then find the odds that a number greater than 11 is drawn.

   4. _____

5. Two marbles are chosen at random from a bag containing 4 red and 3 blue marbles. The table and relative-frequency histogram show the distribution of the number of red marbles chosen. Find $P(R = 2)$.

R = Red	0	1	2
Probability	$\frac{1}{7}$	$\frac{4}{7}$	$\frac{2}{7}$

   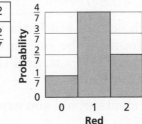

   5. _____

---

12 Chapter 12 Quiz
(Lessons 12–4 and 12–5)

1. A pair of dice is thrown. What is the probability that both dice show a number less than 5?

   1. _____

For Questions 2 and 3, consider a bag that contains 8 red marbles, 5 white marbles, and 2 blue marbles.

2. If 3 marbles are selected in succession with replacement, what is the probability that the marbles are white, blue, and red in that order?

   2. _____

3. If 3 marbles are selected in succession without replacement, what is the probability that the marbles are white, blue, and red in that order?

   3. _____

4. Janet has 3 dimes and 6 nickels in her pocket. She selects 3 coins without replacement. What is the probability that she selects all dimes or all nickels?

   4. _____

5. A card is drawn from a standard deck of 52 playing cards. What is the probability that a heart or face card is drawn? (*Hint*: A face card is a jack, queen, or king.)

   5. _____

12 **Chapter 12 Quiz**
(Lessons 12–6 and 12–7)

1. Find the variance of the data set {13, 16, 17, 18, 16, 12, 14, 12}. Round to the nearest hundredth, if necessary.

1. _____

2. Find the standard deviation for the data in Question 1. Round to the nearest hundredth, if necessary.

2. _____

3. Determine if the data in the table appear to be *positively or negatively skewed* or *normally distributed.*

Family Income and Benefits in 2000	
Income and Benefits	Number of Families (in millions)
less than $50,000	35.8
$50,000–$99,999	24.3
$100,000–$149,999	6.9
$150,000–$199,999	2.0
$200,000 or more	1.9

3. _____

The times a group of high school students wake up on weekday mornings was found to be normally distributed. The mean wake-up time was 6:45 A.M. and the times had a standard deviation of 15 minutes.

4. What percent of the students would you expect to wake up between 6:30 A.M. and 7:00 A.M.?

4. _____

5. If 400 students were surveyed, how many would you expect to wake up between 6:00 A.M. and 7:30 A.M.?

5. _____

- -

12 **Chapter 12 Quiz**
(Lessons 12–8 and 12–9)

For Questions 1 and 2, find each probability if a die is rolled 3 times.

1. _____

1. P(exactly two 4s)   2. P(at most two 4s)

2. _____

3. A batter's probability of getting a hit is $\frac{1}{3}$. In his next 5 times at bat, what is the probability that he will get at least 4 hits?

3. _____

4. Determine whether the situation would produce a random sample and explain your answer: *surveying students on the basketball team to determine the favorite sport of students in your school.*

4. _____

5. In a survey of 50 people, 80% read a newspaper at least once per week. Find the margin of sampling error.

5. _____

12 Chapter 12 Mid-Chapter Test

(Lessons 12–1 through 12–4)

SCORE _____

Part I *Write the letter for the correct answer in the blank at the right of each question.*

1. A company manufactures bicycles in 8 different styles. Each style comes in 7 different colors. How many different bicycles does the company make?

   A. 64   **B.** 49   **C.** 56   **D.** 15   **1.** _____

2. How many ways can 6 children form a line to use the drinking fountain?

   A. 120   **B.** 720   **C.** 36   **D.** 30   **2.** _____

3. Find $P(9, 4)$.

   A. 126   **B.** 15,120   **C.** 36   **D.** 3024   **3.** _____

4. Find $C(10, 8)$.

   A. 1,814,400   **B.** 80   **C.** 90   **D.** 45   **4.** _____

5. The probability that an event will occur is $\frac{2}{7}$. What are the odds that the event will occur?

   A. 2:5   **B.** 5:2   **C.** 2:7   **D.** 2:9   **5.** _____

6. A die is rolled twice. Find $P(4, \text{then } 5)$.

   A. $\frac{1}{30}$ **B.** $\frac{1}{3}$ **C.** $\frac{1}{36}$ **D.** $\frac{5}{9}$ **6.** _____

Part II

7. A jar contains 7 red, 8 blue, and 4 green marbles. What is the probability of choosing 3 blue marbles in a row, if no replacement occurs?

   7. _____

8. A stained glass window has 25 blue pieces and 20 red pieces. If 2 pieces are selected at random, what is $P(2 \text{ red or } 2 \text{ blue})$?

   8. _____

9. **SOCCER** On the all-state soccer team, 5 of the 8 players from the North Region are seniors, and 8 of the 12 players from the South Region are seniors. What is the probability that a randomly-selected student is a senior or is a student from the North Region?

   9. _____

10. How many different arrangements of three folders can be made if you have one green, one red, one blue, and one black folder?

    10. _____

11. A bag contains 6 red dice and 10 blue dice. Two dice are selected at random. Find the probability of selecting one red die and one blue die.

    11. _____

12. How many different groups of 3 students can be formed if there are 20 students in the class?

    12. _____

Glencoe Algebra 2

Assessment

12 Chapter 12 Cumulative Review
(Chapters 1–12)

1. The vertices of RST are $R(-1, -3)$, $S(2, 4)$, and $T(-4, 3)$. The triangle is reflected over the line $y = x$. Find the coordinates of $R'S'T'$. (Lesson 4-4)

1. _____

2. Simplify $(x^2 + 3) - (4x^2 - 5x - 9)$. (Lesson 5-2)

2. _____

3. Determine whether $f(x) = 5x - 8$ and $g(x) = x + \dfrac{8}{5}$ are inverse functions. (Lesson 7-8)

3. _____

4. _____

For Questions 4 and 5, graph the function or equation.

4. $(x + 5)^2 + y^2 = 9$ (Lesson 8-3)

5. $f(x) = -\dfrac{2}{(x - 1)^2}$ (Lesson 9-3)

5.

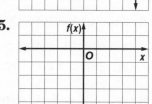

6. Solve $\dfrac{w}{w - 3} + w < \dfrac{3}{w - 3}$. Check your solution(s). (Lesson 9-6)

6. _____

7. Write the equation $\log_{1000} \dfrac{1}{10} = -\dfrac{1}{3}$ in exponential form. (Lesson 10-2)

7. _____

8. A savings account deposit of $500 is to earn 5.7% interest. After how many years will the investment be worth $750? Use $y = a(1 + r)^t$ and round to the nearest tenth. (Lesson 10-6)

8. _____

9. Find the three arithmetic means between 5 and -7. (Lesson 11-1)

9. _____

10. Find four geometric means between 27 and $\dfrac{1}{9}$. (Lesson 11-3)

10. _____

11. Write $0.\overline{627}$ as a fraction. (Lesson 11-5)

11. _____

12. How many different ways can the letters of the word *PERMUTATION* be arranged? (Lesson 12-2)

12. _____

13. Three cards are drawn from a standard deck of cards without replacement. Find the probability of drawing a king, a queen, and another king in that order. (Lesson 12-4)

13. _____

14. The scores on an algebra test are found to be normally distributed. The mean is 72 and the standard deviation is 8. What percent scored between 72 and 88? (Lesson 12-7)

14. _____

15. In a survey of 250 people, 60% took public transportation to work each day. Find the margin of sampling error. (Lesson 12-9)

15. _____

Glencoe Algebra 2

12 **Standardized Test Practice**
(Chapters 1–12)

Part 1: Multiple Choice

Instructions: Fill in the appropriate oval for the best answer.

1. What is the seventh term in the sequence $-\frac{1}{2}, \frac{1}{4}, -\frac{1}{8}, \frac{1}{16}, \ldots$?

   A. $\frac{1}{64}$ **B.** $-\frac{1}{64}$ **C.** $\frac{1}{128}$ **D.** $-\frac{1}{128}$

   1. Ⓐ Ⓑ Ⓒ Ⓓ

2. In the correctly completed addition problem shown, ▲ and ∗ are nonzero digits. What number does ∗ represent?

   E. 5   **F.** 7

   G. 4   **H.** 2

   $$\begin{array}{r} ▲\ 5 \\ ∗\ ▲ \\ 8\ 1 \\ +\ 1\ ▲ \\ \hline 1\ 6\ 0 \end{array}$$

   2. Ⓔ Ⓕ Ⓖ Ⓗ

3. The volume of a rectangular box is 405. The length, width, and height of the box are in the ratio 5 : 3 : 1. What is the total surface area of the box?

   A. 414   **B.** 27   **C.** 54   **D.** 324

   3. Ⓐ Ⓑ Ⓒ Ⓓ

4. In the figure shown, what is the value of r?

   E. 10   **F.** 14

   G. 70   **H.** 7

   4. Ⓔ Ⓕ Ⓖ Ⓗ

5. David is twice as old as his sister, Jennifer. Three years ago, David was three times as old as Jennifer. How old is David now?

   A. 12   **B.** 9   **C.** 6   **D.** 3

   5. Ⓐ Ⓑ Ⓒ Ⓓ

6. If $a < 0$ and $b > 0$, which of the following statements must be true?

   I. $ab < 0$ **II.** $b - a > 0$ **III.** $ac < bc$

   E. I, II, and III   **F.** I only

   G. I and II only   **H.** II and III only

   6. Ⓔ Ⓕ Ⓖ Ⓗ

7. If $(x - y)^2 = 200$ and $x^2 + y^2 = 50$, what is the value of xy?

   A. -75 **B.** 75   **C.** 150   **D.** -150

   7. Ⓐ Ⓑ Ⓒ Ⓓ

8. What is 25% of 20% of $\frac{3}{4}$?

   E. 0.375   **F.** 3.75   **G.** 0.00375   **H.** 0.0375

   8. Ⓔ Ⓕ Ⓖ Ⓗ

9. What is the sum of all composite numbers between 1 and 15?

   A. 120   **B.** 59   **C.** 78   **D.** 63

   9. Ⓐ Ⓑ Ⓒ Ⓓ

10. If $(x + y)^2 = 8$ and $(x - y)^2 = 4$, what is xy?

    E. 0   **F.** 1   **G.** 2   **H.** 3

    10. Ⓔ Ⓕ Ⓖ Ⓗ

Assessment

12 **Standardized Test Practice** *(continued)*

Part 2: Grid In

Instructions: Enter your answer by writing each digit of the answer in a column box and then shading in the appropriate oval that corresponds to that entry.

11. Alejandra has been saving to purchase a VCR. The model she wants is priced at $180, on which she will be required to pay 5% sales tax. She has already saved $53. If Alejandra earns $8.50 per hour after all payroll deductions have been made, for how many hours will she need to work in order to have enough money to purchase the VCR?

11. 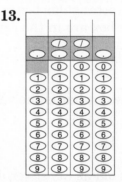 **12.**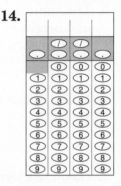

12. If $4^{3x-2} = 256$, what is the value of 3^{2x+1}?

13. In the figure at the right, quadrilaterals $ABCD$ and $RSTU$ are similar. What is the value of n?

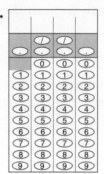

14. If the average of a and b is 87, the average of a and c is 73, and the average of b and c is 50, what is the average of $a, b,$ and c?

13. 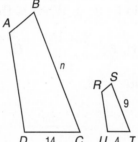 **14.**

Part 3: Quantitative Comparison

Instructions: Compare the quantities in columns A and B. Shade in
 (A) if the quantity in column A is greater;
 (B) if the quantity in column B is greater;
 (C) if the quantities are equal; or
 (D) if the relationship cannot be determined from the information given.

Column A	Column B	
	$d + 4 < 0$	**15.** (A) (B) (C) (D)
15. $3d$	d^3	
	$y < -1, z > 5$	**16.** (A) (B) (C) (D)
16. $\dfrac{z-y}{z}$	$-\dfrac{z}{y} + 1$	
	$h \neq 0$	**17.** (A) (B) (C) (D)
17. $\dfrac{4h^4 + h}{h}$	$4h^3 + 1$	

Unit 4 Test
(Chapters 11–12)

1. Find the next four terms of the arithmetic sequence
   4, 10, 16, ...

   1. _____

2. Find the three arithmetic means between 21 and 13.

   2. _____

3. Find S_n for the arithmetic series in which $a_1 = -11$, $a_n = 13$,
   and $n = 7$.

   3. _____

4. Find the next two terms of the geometric sequence
   6250, 5000, 4000, ...

   4. _____

5. Find four geometric means between 4096 and 972.

   5. _____

6. Find the sum of a geometric series for which $a_1 = 1$, $r = 2$,
   and $n = 6$.

   6. _____

7. Find a_1 in a geometric series for which $S_n = 189$, $r = \frac{1}{2}$, and
   $a_n = 3$.

   7. _____

8. Find the sum of the infinite geometric series
   $36 + 24 + 16 + ...$, if it exists.

   8. _____

9. Write $0.\overline{735}$ as a fraction.

   9. _____

10. Find the first five terms of the sequence for which $a_1 = 5$
    and $a_{n+1} = 3a_n + 1$.

    10. _____

11. Find the first three iterates x_1, x_2, x_3 of $f(x) = 2x - 5$ for
    an initial value of $x_0 = 3$.

    11. _____

12. Use the Binomial Theorem to find the fifth term in the
    expansion of $(2x + 3y)^5$.

    12. _____

13. Prove that the statement $\frac{1}{5} + \frac{1}{5^2} + \frac{1}{5^3} + ... + \frac{1}{5^n} = \frac{1}{4}\left(1 - \frac{1}{5^n}\right)$
    is true for all positive integers n. Write your proof on a
    separate piece of paper.

    13. _____

14. Find a counterexample to the statement $4^n + 1$ is divisible
    by 5.

    14. _____

15. A scout troop will prepare trail mix for their next hike.
    They have decided to mix one type of nut, one type of dried
    fruit, and one type of granola. The local store carries 8 types
    of nuts, 6 types of dried fruit, and 5 types of granola. How
    many different trail mixes are possible?

    15. _____

16. Students are given a list of ten vocabulary words to learn. In
    how many ways could four of the words be listed on a test?

    16. _____

Assessment

Unit 4 Test (continued)
(Chapters 11–12)

17. Evaluate $C(12, 10)$.

17. _____

18. If the probability that an event will occur is $\frac{8}{13}$, what are the odds that it will occur?

18. _____

19. A red die and a blue die are tossed. What is the probability that the red die shows an odd number and the blue die shows a 1 or 2?

19. _____

20. From a group of 6 men and 4 women, a committee of 3 is to be selected at random. Find P(at least 2 women).

20. _____

21. Two cards are drawn from a standard deck of cards. Find the probability that a king or a red card is drawn.

21. _____

For Questions 22 and 23, use the data in the table that shows the number of public secondary schools in eight eastern states in the fall of 1998.

22. Find the mean, median, mode, and standard deviation of the data. Round to the nearest hundredth, if necessary.

22. _____

State	Number of Public Secondary Schools
Florida	456
Georgia	306
Maine	160
Massachusetts	363
North Carolina	376
New York	935
Rhode Island	54
Virginia	349

Source: *World Almanac*

23. Determine whether the data in the table appear to be *positively skewed*, *negatively skewed*, or *normally distributed*.

23. _____

24. The time a group of high school students arrive home from school each day was found to be normally distributed. The mean time was 3:15 P.M. and the times had a standard deviation of 15 minutes. What is the probability that a student chosen at random arrives home from school before 2:30 P.M.?

24. _____

25. During a clothing sale, $\frac{1}{4}$ of the store merchandise is reduced in price. Find the probability that 3 of 5 randomly-selected shirts have reduced prices.

25. _____

26. Determine whether the situation would produce a random sample and explain your answer: *surveying people at a concert to determine their favorite local radio station.*

26. _____

12 Standardized Test Practice

Student Record Sheet (Use with pages 694–695 of the Student Edition.)

Part 1 Multiple Choice

Select the best answer from the choices given and fill in the corresponding oval.

1 Ⓐ Ⓑ Ⓒ Ⓓ   4 Ⓐ Ⓑ Ⓒ Ⓓ   7 Ⓐ Ⓑ Ⓒ Ⓓ   9 Ⓐ Ⓑ Ⓒ Ⓓ

2 Ⓐ Ⓑ Ⓒ Ⓓ   5 Ⓐ Ⓑ Ⓒ Ⓓ   8 Ⓐ Ⓑ Ⓒ Ⓓ   10 Ⓐ Ⓑ Ⓒ Ⓓ

3 Ⓐ Ⓑ Ⓒ Ⓓ   6 Ⓐ Ⓑ Ⓒ Ⓓ

Part 2 Short Response/Grid In

Solve the problem and write your answer in the blank.

Also enter your answer by writing each number or symbol in a box. Then fill in the corresponding oval for that number or symbol.

11 _____

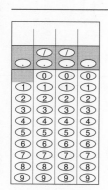

12 _____

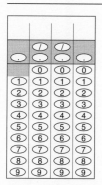

13 _____

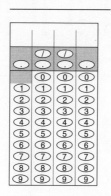

14 _____

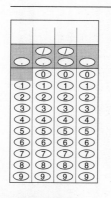

15 _____

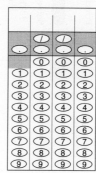

Part 3 Quantitative Comparison

Select the best answer from the choices given and fill in the corresponding oval.

16 Ⓐ Ⓑ Ⓒ Ⓓ   18 Ⓐ Ⓑ Ⓒ Ⓓ   20 Ⓐ Ⓑ Ⓒ Ⓓ

17 Ⓐ Ⓑ Ⓒ Ⓓ   19 Ⓐ Ⓑ Ⓒ Ⓓ   21 Ⓐ Ⓑ Ⓒ Ⓓ

Answers

12-1 Study Guide and Intervention (continued)

The Counting Principle

Dependent Events If the outcome of an event *does* affect the outcome of another event, the two events are said to be **dependent**. The Fundamental Counting Principle still applies.

Example **ENTERTAINMENT** The guests at a sleepover brought 8 videos. They decided they would only watch 3 videos. **How many orders of 3 different videos are possible?**

After the group chooses to watch a video, they will not choose to watch it again, so the choices of videos are dependent events.

There are 8 choices for the first video. That leaves 7 choices for the second. After they choose the first 2 videos, there are 6 remaining choices. Thus by the Fundamental Counting Principle, there are $8 \cdot 7 \cdot 6$ or 336 orders of 3 different videos.

Exercises

Solve each problem.

1. Three students are scheduled to give oral reports on Monday. In how many ways can their presentations be ordered? **6**

2. In how many ways can the first five letters of the alphabet be arranged if each letter is used only once? **120**

3. In how many different ways can 4 different books be arranged on the shelf? **24**

4. How many license plates consisting of three letters followed by three numbers are possible when no repetition is allowed? **11,232,000**

5. Sixteen teams are competing in a soccer match. Gold, silver, and bronze medals will be awarded to the top three finishers. In how many ways can the medals be awarded? **3360**

6. In a word-building game each player picks 7 letter tiles. If Julio's letters are all different, how many 3-letter combinations can he make out of his 7 letters? **210**

7. The editor has accepted 6 articles for the news letter. In how many ways can the 6 articles be ordered? **720**

8. There are 10 one-hour workshops scheduled for the open house at the greenhouse. There is only one conference room available. In how many ways can the workshops be ordered? **3,628,800**

9. The top 5 runners at the cross-country meet will receive trophies. If there are 22 runners in the race, in how many ways can the trophies be awarded? **3,160,080**

Lesson 12-1

12-1 Study Guide and Intervention

The Counting Principle

Independent Events If the outcome of one event does not affect the outcome of another event and vice versa, the events are called **independent events.**

Fundamental Counting Principle	If event *M* can occur in *m* ways and is followed by event *N* that can occur in *n* ways, then the event *M* followed by the event *N* can occur in $m \cdot n$ ways.

Example **FOOD** For the Breakfast Special at the Country Pantry, customers can choose their eggs scrambled, fried, or poached, whole wheat or white toast, and either orange, apple, tomato, or grapefruit juice. **How many different Breakfast Specials can a customer order?**

A customer's choice of eggs does not affect his or her choice of toast or juice, so the events are independent. There are 3 ways to choose eggs, 2 ways to choose toast, and 4 ways to choose juice. By the Fundamental Counting Principle, there are $3 \cdot 2 \cdot 4$ or 24 ways to choose the Breakfast Special.

Exercises

Solve each problem.

1. The Palace of Pizza offers small, medium, or large pizzas with 14 different toppings available. How many different one-topping pizzas do they serve? **42**

2. The letters A, B, C, and D are used to form four-letter passwords for entering a computer file. How many passwords are possible if letters can be repeated? **256**

3. A restaurant serves 5 main dishes, 3 salads, and 4 desserts. How many different meals could be ordered if each has a main dish, a salad, and a dessert? **60**

4. Marissa brought 8 T-shirts and 6 pairs of shorts to summer camp. How many different outfits consisting of a T-shirt and a pair of shorts does she have? **48**

5. There are 6 different packages available for school pictures. The studio offers 5 different backgrounds and 2 different finishes. How many different options are available? **60**

6. How many 5-digit even numbers can be formed using the digits 4, 6, 7, 2, 8 if digits can be repeated? **2500**

7. How many license plate numbers consisting of three letters followed by three numbers are possible when repetition is allowed? **17,576,000**

8. How many 4-digit positive even integers are there? **4500**

12-1 Skills Practice

The Counting Principle

State whether the events are independent or dependent.

1. finishing in first, second, or third place in a ten-person race **dependent**

2. choosing a pizza size and a topping for the pizza **independent**

3. Seventy-five raffle tickets are placed in a jar. Three tickets are then selected, one after the other, without replacing a ticket after it is chosen. **dependent**

4. The 232 members of the freshman class all vote by secret ballot for the class representative to the Student Senate. **independent**

Solve each problem.

5. A surveying firm plans to buy a color printer for printing its maps. It has narrowed its choice to one of three models. Each of the models is available with either 32 megabytes of random access memory (RAM), 64 megabytes of RAM, or 128 megabytes of RAM. From how many combinations of models and RAM does the firm have to choose? **9**

6. How many arrangements of three letters can be formed from the letters of the word *MATH* if any letter will not be used more than once? **24**

7. Allan is playing the role of Oliver in his school's production of *Oliver Twist*. The wardrobe crew has presented Allan with 5 pairs of pants and 4 shirts that he can wear. How many possible costumes consisting of a pair of pants and a shirt does Allan have to choose from? **20**

8. The 10-member steering committee that is preparing a study of the public transportation needs of its town will select a chairperson, vice-chairperson, and secretary from the committee. No person can serve in more than one position. In how many ways can the three positions be filled? **720**

9. Jeanine has decided to buy a pickup truck. Her choices include either a V-6 engine or a V-8 engine, a standard cab or an extended cab, and 2-wheel drive or 4-wheel drive. How many possible models does she have to choose from? **8**

10. A mail-order company that sells gardening tools offers rakes in two different lengths. Customers can also choose either a wooden, plastic, or fiberglass handle for the rake. How many different kinds of rakes can a customer buy? **6**

11. A Mexican restaurant offers chicken, beef, or vegetarian fajitas wrapped with either corn or flour tortillas, and topped with either mild, medium, or hot salsa. How many different choices of fajitas does a customer have? **18**

12-1 Practice (Average)

The Counting Principle

State whether the events are independent or dependent.

1. choosing an ice cream flavor and choosing a topping for the ice cream **independent**

2. choosing an offensive player of the game and a defensive player of the game in a professional football game **independent**

3. From 15 entries in an art contest, a camp counselor chooses first, second, and third place winners. **dependent**

4. Jillian is selecting two more courses for her block schedule next semester. She must select one of three morning history classes and one of two afternoon math classes. **independent**

Solve each problem.

5. A briefcase lock has 3 rotating cylinders, each containing 10 digits. How many numerical codes are possible? **1000**

6. A golf club manufacturer makes irons with 7 different shaft lengths, 3 different grips, 5 different lies, and 2 different club head materials. How many different combinations are offered? **210**

7. There are five different routes that a commuter can take from her home to the office. In how many ways can she make a round trip if she uses a different route coming than going? **20**

8. In how many ways can the four call letters of a radio station be arranged if the first letter must be W or K and no letters repeat? **27,600**

9. How many 7-digit phone numbers can be formed if the first digit cannot be 0 or 1, and any digit can be repeated? **8,000,000**

10. How many 7-digit phone numbers can be formed if the first digit cannot be 0, and any digit can be repeated? **9,000,000**

11. How many 7-digit phone numbers can be formed if the first digit cannot be 0 or 1, and if no digit can be repeated? **483,840**

12. How many 7-digit phone numbers can be formed if the first digit cannot be 0, and if no digit can be repeated? **544,320**

13. How many 6-character passwords can be formed if the first character is a digit and the remaining 5 characters are letters that can be repeated? **118,813,760**

14. How many 6-character passwords can be formed if the first and last characters are digits and the remaining characters are letters? Assume that any character can be repeated. **45,697,600**

Lesson 12-1

Answers

12-1 Reading to Learn Mathematics

The Counting Principle

Pre-Activity How can you count the maximum number of license plates a state can issue?

Read the introduction to Lesson 12-1 at the top of page 632 in your textbook.

Assume that all Florida license plates have three letters followed by three digits, and that there are no rules against using the same letter or number more than once. How many choices are there for each letter? for each digit?
26; 10

Reading the Lesson

1. Shamim is signing up for her classes. Most of her classes are required, but she has two electives. For her arts class, she can chose between Art, Band, Chorus, or Drama. For her language class, she can choose between French, German, and Spanish.

   a. To organize her choices, Shamim decides to make a tree diagram. Let A, B, C, and D represent Art, Band, Chorus, and Drama, and F, G, and S represent French, German, and Spanish. Complete the following diagram.

   b. How could Shamim have found the number of possible combinations without making a tree diagram? **Sample answer: Multiply the number of choices for her arts class by the number of choices for her language class: 4 × 3 = 12.**

2. A jar contains 6 red marbles, 4 blue marbles, and 3 yellow marbles. Indicate whether the events described are *dependent* or *independent*.

   a. A marble is drawn out of the jar and is not replaced. A second marble is drawn. **dependent**

   b. A marble is drawn out of the jar and is put back in. The jar is shaken. A second marble is drawn. **independent**

Helping You Remember

3. One definition of *independent* is "not determined or influenced by someone or something else." How can this definition help you remember the difference between *independent* and *dependent* events? **Sample answer: If the outcome of one event does *not* affect or influence the outcome of another, the events are independent. If the outcome of one event *does* affect or influence the outcome of another, the events are dependent.**

12-1 Enrichment

Tree Diagrams and the Power Rule

If you flip a coin once, there are two possible outcomes: heads showing (H) or tails showing (T). The tree diagram to the right shows the four (2^2) possible outcomes if you flip a coin twice.

Flip 1	Flip 2	Outcomes
	H	HH
H	T	HT
T	H	TH
	T	TT

start

Example 1 Draw a tree diagram to show all the possible outcomes for flipping a coin three times. List the outcomes.

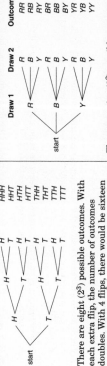

Flip 1	Flip 2	Flip 3	Outcomes
		H	HHH
	H	T	HHT
H		H	HTH
	T	T	HTT
		H	THH
	H	T	THT
T		H	TTH
	T	T	TTT

start

There are eight (2^3) possible outcomes. With each extra flip, the number of outcomes doubles. With 4 flips, there would be sixteen (2^4) outcomes.

The Power Rule for the number of outcomes states that if an experiment is repeated n times, and if there are b possible outcomes each time, there are b^n total possible outcomes.

Example 2 In a cup there are a red, a blue, and a yellow marble. How many possible outcomes are there if you draw one marble at random, replace it, and then draw another?

Draw 1	Draw 2	Outcomes
	R	RR
R	B	RB
	Y	RY
	R	BR
B	B	BB
	Y	BY
	R	YR
Y	B	YB
	Y	YY

start

There are nine (3^2) possible outcomes.

Find the total number of possible outcomes for each experiment. Use tree diagrams to help you.

1. flipping a coin 5 times 2^5

2. doing the marble experiment 6 times 3^6

3. flipping a coin 8 times 2^8

4. rolling a 6-sided die 2 times 6^2

5. rolling a 6-sided die 3 times 6^3

6. rolling a 4-sided die 2 times 4^2

7. rolling a 4-sided die 3 times 4^3

8. rolling a 12-sided die 2 times 12^2

Page 705

12-2 Study Guide and Intervention

Permutations and Combinations

Permutations When a group of objects or people are arranged in a certain order, the arrangement is called a **permutation**.

Permutations	The number of permutations of n distinct objects taken r at a time is given by $P(n, r) = \dfrac{n!}{(n-r)!}$.
Permutations with Repetitions	The number of permutations of n objects of which p are alike and q are alike is $\dfrac{n!}{p!q!}$.

The rule for permutations with repetitions can be extended to any number of objects that are repeated.

Example From a list of 20 books, each student must choose 4 books for book reports. The first report is a traditional book report, the second a poster, the third a newspaper interview with one of the characters, and the fourth a timeline of the plot. How many different orderings of books can be chosen?

Since each book report has a different format, order is important. You must find the number of permutations of 20 objects taken 4 at a time.

$P(n, r) = \dfrac{n!}{(n-r)!}$ Permutation formula

$P(20, 4) = \dfrac{20!}{(20-4)!}$ $n = 20, r = 4$

$= \dfrac{20!}{16!}$ Simplify.

$= \dfrac{20 \cdot 19 \cdot 18 \cdot 17 \cdot \cancel{16} \cdot \cancel{15} \cdot \ldots \cdot \cancel{1}}{\cancel{16} \cdot \cancel{15} \cdot \ldots \cdot \cancel{1}}$ Divide by common factors.

$= 116,280$

Books for the book reports can be chosen 116,280 ways.

Exercises

Evaluate each expression.

1. $P(6, 3)$ **120** **2.** $P(8, 5)$ **6720** **3.** $P(9, 4)$ **3024** **4.** $P(11, 6)$ **332,640**

How many different ways can the letters of each word be arranged?

5. MOM **3** **6.** MONDAY **720** **7.** STEREO **360**

8. SCHOOL The high school chorus has been practicing 12 songs, but there is time for only 5 of them at the spring concert. How many different orderings of 5 songs are possible? **95,040**

Page 706

12-2 Study Guide and Intervention (continued)

Permutations and Combinations

Combinations An arrangement or selection of objects in which order is *not* important is called a combination.

Combinations	The number of combinations of n distinct objects taken r at a time is given by $C(n, r) = \dfrac{n!}{(n-r)!r!}$.

Example 1 SCHOOL How many groups of 4 students can be selected from a class of 20?

Since the order of choosing the students is not important, you must find the number of combinations of 20 students taken 4 at a time.

$C(n, r) = \dfrac{n!}{(n-r)!r!}$ Combination formula

$C(20, 4) = \dfrac{20!}{(20-4)!4!}$ $n = 20, r = 4$

$= \dfrac{20!}{16!4!}$ or 4845

There are 4845 possible ways to choose 4 students.

Example 2 In how many ways can you choose 1 vowel and 2 consonants from a set of 26 letter tiles? (Assume there are 5 vowels and 21 consonants.)

By the Fundamental Counting Principle, you can multiply the number of ways to select one vowel and the number of ways to select 2 consonants. Only the letters chosen matter, not the order in which they were chosen, so use combinations.

$C(5, 1)$ One of 5 vowels are drawn.
$C(21, 2)$ Two of 21 consonants are drawn.

$C(5, 1) \cdot C(21, 2) = \dfrac{5!}{(5-1)!1!} \cdot \dfrac{21!}{(21-2)!2!}$ Combination formula

$= \dfrac{5!}{4!} \cdot \dfrac{21!}{19!2!}$ Subtract.

$= 5 \cdot 210$ or 1050 Simplify.

There are 1050 combinations of 1 vowel and 2 consonants.

Exercises

Evaluate each expression.

1. $C(5, 3)$ **10** **2.** $C(7, 4)$ **35** **3.** $C(15, 7)$ **6435** **4.** $C(10, 5)$ **252**

5. PLAYING CARDS From a standard deck of 52 cards, in how many ways can 5 cards be drawn? **2,598,960**

6. HOCKEY How many hockey teams of 6 players can be formed from 14 players without regard to position played? **3003**

7. COMMITTEES From a group of 10 men and 12 women, how many committees of 5 men and 6 women can be formed? **232,848**

Answers

12-2 Practice (Average)

Permutations and Combinations

Evaluate each expression.

1. $P(8, 6)$ 20,160
2. $P(9, 7)$ 181,440
3. $P(3, 3)$ 6
4. $P(4, 3)$ 24
5. $P(4, 1)$ 4
6. $P(7, 2)$ 42
7. $C(8, 2)$ 28
8. $C(11, 3)$ 165
9. $C(20, 18)$ 190
10. $C(9, 9)$ 1
11. $C(3, 1)$ 3
12. $C(9, 3) \cdot C(6, 2)$ 1260

Determine whether each situation involves a *permutation* or a *combination*. Then find the number of possibilities.

13. selecting a 4-person bobsled team from a group of 9 athletes combination; 126
14. an arrangement of the letters in the word *Canada* permutation; 120
15. arranging 4 charms on a bracelet that has a clasp, a front, and a back permutation; 24
16. selecting 3 desserts from 10 desserts that are displayed on a dessert cart in a restaurant combination; 120
17. an arrangement of the letters in the word *annually* permutation; 5040
18. forming a 2-person sales team from a group of 12 salespeople combination; 66
19. making 5-sided polygons by choosing any 5 of 11 points located on a circle to be the vertices combination; 462
20. seating 5 men and 5 women alternately in a row, beginning with a woman permutation; 14,400
21. **STUDENT GROUPS** Farmington High is planning its academic festival. All math classes will send 2 representatives to compete in the math bowl. How many different groups of students can be chosen from a class of 16 students? 120
22. **PHOTOGRAPHY** A photographer is taking pictures of a bride and groom and their 6 attendants. If she takes photographs of 3 people in a group, how many different groups can she photograph? 56
23. **AIRLINES** An airline is hiring 5 flight attendants. If 8 people apply for the job, how many different groups of 5 attendants can the airline hire? 56
24. **SUBSCRIPTIONS** A school librarian would like to buy subscriptions to 7 new magazines. Her budget, however, will allow her to buy only 4 new subscriptions. How many different groups of 4 magazines can she choose from the 7 magazines? 35

Lesson 12-2

12-2 Skills Practice

Permutations and Combinations

Evaluate each expression.

1. $P(6, 3)$ 120
2. $P(8, 2)$ 56
3. $P(2, 1)$ 2
4. $P(3, 2)$ 6
5. $P(10, 4)$ 5040
6. $P(5, 5)$ 120
7. $C(2, 2)$ 1
8. $C(5, 3)$ 10
9. $C(4, 1)$ 4
10. $C(8, 7)$ 8
11. $C(3, 2)$ 3
12. $C(7, 4)$ 35

Determine whether each situation involves a *permutation* or a *combination*. Then find the number of possibilities.

13. seating 8 students in 8 seats in the front row of the school auditorium permutation; 40,320
14. introducing the 5 starting players on the Woodsville High School basketball team at the beginning of the next basketball game permutation; 120
15. checking out 3 library books from a list of 8 books for a research paper combination; 56
16. choosing 2 movies to rent from 5 movies combination; 10
17. the first-, second-, and third-place finishers in a race with 10 contestants permutation; 720
18. electing 4 candidates to a municipal planning board from a field of 7 candidates combination; 35
19. choosing 2 vegetables from a menu that offers 6 vegetable choices combination; 15
20. an arrangement of the letters in the word *rhombus* permutation; 5040
21. selecting 2 of 8 choices of orange juice at a store combination; 28
22. placing a red rose bush, a yellow rose bush, a white rose bush, and a pink rose bush in a row in a planter permutation; 24
23. selecting 2 of 9 kittens at an animal rescue shelter combination; 36
24. an arrangement of the letters in the word *isosceles* permutation; 30,240

Left Page

12-2 **Reading to Learn Mathematics**

Permutations and Combinations

Pre-Activity How do permutations and combinations apply to softball?

Read the introduction to Lesson 12-2 at the top of page 638 in your textbook.

Suppose that 20 students enter a math contest. In how many ways can first, second, and third places be awarded? (Write your answer as a product. Do not calculate the product.) **20 · 19 · 18**

Reading the Lesson

1. Indicate whether each situation involves a *permutation* or a *combination*.

   a. choosing five students from a class to work on a special project **combination**

   b. arranging five pictures in a row on a wall **permutation**

   c. drawing a hand of 13 cards from a 52-card deck **combination**

   d. arranging the letters of the word *algebra* **permutation**

2. Write an expression that can be used to calculate each of the following.

   a. number of combinations of *n* distinct objects taken *r* at a time $\dfrac{n!}{(n-r)!r!}$

   b. number of permutations of *n* objects of which *p* are alike and *q* are alike $\dfrac{n!}{p!q!}$

   c. number of permutations of *n* distinct objects taken *r* at a time $\dfrac{n!}{(n-r)!}$

3. Five cards are drawn from a standard deck of cards. Suppose you are asked to determine how many possible hands consist of one heart, two diamonds, and two spades.

   a. Which of the following would you use to solve this problem: *Fundamental Counting Principle*, *permutations*, or *combinations*? (More than one of these may apply.)

   Fundamental Counting Principle, combinations

   b. Write an expression that involves the notation $P(n, r)$ and/or $C(n, r)$ that you would use to solve this problem. (Do not do any calculations.)

   $C(13, 1) \cdot C(13, 2) \cdot C(13, 2)$

Helping You Remember

4. Many students have trouble knowing when to use permutations and when to use combinations to solve counting problems. How can the idea of *order* help you to remember the difference between permutations and combinations?

   Sample answer: A permutation is an arrangement of objects in which order is important. A combination is a selection of objects in which order is *not* important.

Right Page

12-2 **Enrichment**

Combinations and Pascal's Triangle

Pascal's triangle is a special array of numbers invented by Blaise Pascal (1623–1662). The values in Pascal's triangle can be found using the combinations shown below.

1. Evaluate the expression in each cell of the triangle.

C(1,0)	C(1,1)				
1	1				

C(2,0)	C(2,1)	C(2,2)
1	2	1

C(3,0)	C(3,1)	C(3,2)	C(3,3)
1	3	3	1

C(4,0)	C(4,1)	C(4,2)	C(4,3)	C(4,4)
1	4	6	4	1

C(5,0)	C(5,1)	C(5,2)	C(5,3)	C(5,4)	C(5,5)
1	5	10	10	5	1

2. The pattern shows the relationship between $C(n, r)$ and Pascal's triangle. In general, it is true that $C(n, r) + C(n, r + 1) = C(n + 1, r + 1)$. Complete the proof of this property. In each step, the denominator has been given.

$$C(n, r) + C(n, r + 1) = \frac{n!}{r!(n-r)!} + \frac{n!}{(r+1)!(n-r-1)!}$$

$$= \frac{n!(r+1)}{r!(n-r)!(r+1)} + \frac{n!(n-r)}{(r+1)!(n-r-1)!(n-r)}$$

$$= \frac{n!(r+1)}{(r+1)!(n-r)!} + \frac{n!(n-r)}{(r+1)!(n-r)!}$$

$$= \frac{n!(r+1+n-r)}{(r+1)!(n-r)!}$$

$$= \frac{n!(n+1)}{(r+1)!(n-r)!}$$

$$= \frac{(n+1)!}{(r+1)!(n-r)!}$$

$$= \frac{(n+1)!}{(r+1)!((n+1)-(r+1))!}$$

$$= C(n+1, r+1)$$

Answers

12-3 Study Guide and Intervention (continued)
Probability

Probability Distributions A random variable is a variable whose value is the numerical outcome of a random event. A **probability distribution** for a particular random variable is a function that maps the sample space to the probabilities of the outcomes in the sample space.

Example Suppose two dice are rolled. The table and the relative-frequency histogram show the distribution of the absolute value of the difference of the numbers rolled. Use the graph to determine which outcome is the most likely. What is its probability?

Difference	0	1	2	3	4	5
Probability	$\frac{1}{6}$	$\frac{5}{18}$	$\frac{2}{9}$	$\frac{1}{6}$	$\frac{1}{9}$	$\frac{1}{18}$

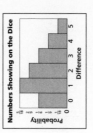

Numbers Showing on the Dice

The greatest probability in the graph is $\frac{5}{18}$.
The most likely outcome is a difference of 1 and its probability is $\frac{5}{18}$.

Exercises

Four coins are tossed.

1. Complete the table below to show the probability distribution of the number of heads.

Number of Heads	0	1	2	3	4
Probability	$\frac{1}{16}$	$\frac{1}{4}$	$\frac{3}{8}$	$\frac{1}{4}$	$\frac{1}{16}$

2. Make relative-frequency distribution of the data.

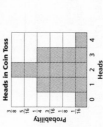

Heads in Coin Toss

 Glencoe Algebra 2

12-3 Study Guide and Intervention
Probability

Probability and Odds In probability, a desired outcome is called a **success**; any other outcome is called a **failure**.

Probability of Success and Failure	If an event can succeed in *s* ways and fail in *r* ways, then the probabilities of success, $P(S)$, and of failure, $P(F)$, are as follows. $P(S) = \frac{s}{s+f}$ and $P(F) = \frac{f}{s+f}$.
Definition of Odds	If an event can succeed in *s* ways and fail in *r* ways, then the odds of success and of failure are as follows. Odds of success = $s{:}f$ Odds of failure = $f{:}s$

Example 1 **When 3 coins are tossed, what is the probability that at least 2 are heads?**

You can use a tree diagram to find the sample space.

First Coin	Second Coin	Third Coin	Possible Outcomes
		H	HHH
	H	T	HHT
		H	HTH
H	T	T	HTT
		H	THH
	H	T	THT
		H	TTH
T	T	T	TTT

Of the 8 possible outcomes, 4 have at least 2 heads. So the probability of tossing at least 2 heads is $\frac{4}{8}$ or $\frac{1}{2}$.

Example 2 **What is the probability of picking 4 fiction books and 2 biographies from a best-seller list that consists of 12 fiction books and 6 biographies?**

By the Fundamental Counting Principle, the number of successes is $C(12, 4) \cdot C(6, 2)$. The total number of selections, $s + f$, of 6 books is $C(18, 6)$.

$$P(4 \text{ fiction, 2 biography}) = \frac{C(12, 4) \cdot C(6, 2)}{C(18, 6)} \text{ or about } 0.40$$

The probability of selecting 4 fiction books and 2 biographies is about 40%.

Exercises

Find the odds of an event occurring, given the probability of the event.

1. $\frac{3}{7}$ 3:4
2. $\frac{4}{5}$ 4:1
3. $\frac{2}{13}$ 2:11
4. $1\frac{1}{15}$ 1:14

Find the probability of an event occurring, given the odds of the event.

5. 10:1 $\frac{10}{11}$
6. 2:5 $\frac{2}{7}$
7. 4:9 $\frac{4}{13}$
8. 8:3 $\frac{8}{11}$

One bag of candy contains 15 red candies, 10 yellow candies, and 6 green candies. Find the probability of each selection.

9. picking a red candy $\frac{15}{31}$
10. not picking a yellow candy $\frac{21}{31}$
11. picking a green candy $\frac{6}{31}$
12. not picking a red candy $\frac{16}{31}$

 Glencoe Algebra 2

Lesson 12-3

NAME _____ DATE _____ PERIOD _____

12-3 Skills Practice
Probability

Ahmed is posting 2 photographs on his website. He has narrowed his choices to 4 landscape photographs and 3 portraits. If he chooses the two photographs at random, find the probability of each selection.

1. P(2 portrait) $\frac{1}{7}$ 2. P(2 landscape) $\frac{2}{7}$ 3. P(1 of each) $\frac{4}{7}$

The Carubas have a collection of 28 video movies, including 12 westerns and 16 science fiction. Elise selects 3 of the movies at random to bring to a sleep-over at her friend's house. Find the probability of each selection.

4. P(3 westerns) $\frac{55}{819}$ 5. P(3 science fiction) $\frac{20}{117}$

6. P(1 western and 2 science fiction) $\frac{40}{91}$ 7. P(2 westerns and 1 science fiction) $\frac{88}{273}$

8. P(3 comedy) 0   9. P(2 science fiction and 2 westerns) 0

For Exercises 10–13, use the chart that shows the class and gender statistics for the students taking an Algebra 1 or Algebra 2 class at La Mesa High School.

If a student taking Algebra 1 or Algebra 2 is selected at random, find each probability. Express as decimals rounded to the nearest thousandth.

Class/Gender	Number
Freshman/Male	95
Freshman/Female	101
Sophomore/Male	154
Sophomore/Female	145
Junior/Male	100
Junior/Female	102

10. P(sophomore/female) 0.208
11. P(junior/male) 0.143
12. P(freshman/male) 0.136
13. P(freshman/female) 0.145

Find the odds of an event occurring, given the probability of the event.

14. $\frac{5}{8}$ 5:3   15. $\frac{2}{7}$ 2:5   16. $\frac{3}{5}$ 3:2

17. $\frac{1}{10}$ 1:9   18. $\frac{5}{6}$ 5:1   19. $\frac{5}{12}$ 5:7

Find the probability of an event occurring, given the odds of the event.

20. 2:1 $\frac{2}{3}$ 21. 8:9 $\frac{8}{17}$ 22. 4:1 $\frac{4}{5}$

23. 1:9 $\frac{1}{10}$ 24. 2:7 $\frac{2}{9}$ 25. 5:9 $\frac{5}{14}$

© Glencoe/McGraw-Hill 713 Glencoe Algebra 2

Lesson 12-3

NAME _____ DATE _____ PERIOD _____

12-3 Practice (Average)
Probability

A bag contains 1 green, 4 red, and 5 yellow balls. Two balls are selected at random. Find the probability of each selection.

1. P(2 red) $\frac{2}{15}$ 2. P(1 red and 1 yellow) $\frac{4}{9}$ 3. P(1 green and 1 yellow) $\frac{1}{9}$

4. P(2 green) 0   5. P(2 red and 1 yellow) 0   6. P(1 red and 1 green) $\frac{4}{45}$

A bank contains 3 pennies, 8 nickels, 4 dimes, and 10 quarters. Two coins are selected at random. Find the probability of each selection.

7. P(2 pennies) $\frac{1}{100}$ 8. P(2 dimes) $\frac{1}{50}$ 9. P(1 nickel and 1 dime) $\frac{8}{75}$

10. P(1 quarter and 1 penny) $\frac{1}{10}$ 11. P(1 quarter and 1 nickel) $\frac{4}{15}$ 12. P(2 dimes and 1 quarter) 0

Henrico visits a home decorating store to choose wallpapers for his new house. The store has 28 books of wallpaper samples, including 10 books of WallPride samples and 18 books of Deluxe Wall Coverings samples. The store will allow Henrico to bring 4 books home for a few days so he can decide which wallpapers he wants to buy. If Henrico randomly chooses 4 books to bring home, find the probability of each selection.

13. P(4 WallPride) $\frac{2}{195}$ 14. P(2 WallPride and 2 Deluxe) $\frac{153}{455}$

15. P(1 WallPride and 3 Deluxe) $\frac{544}{1365}$ 16. P(3 WallPride and 1 Deluxe) $\frac{48}{455}$

For Exercises 17–20, use the table that shows the range of verbal SAT scores for freshmen at a small liberal arts college. If a freshman student is chosen at random, find each probability. Express as decimals rounded to the nearest thousandth.

Range	400–449	450–499	500–549	550–559	600–649	650+
Number of Students	129	275	438	602	620	412

17. P(400–449) 0.052   18. P(550–559) 0.243   19. P(at least 650) 0.166

Find the odds of an event occurring, given the probability of the event.

20. $\frac{4}{11}$ 4:7   21. $\frac{12}{13}$ 12:1   22. $\frac{5}{99}$ 5:94   23. $\frac{1}{1000}$ 1:999

24. $\frac{5}{16}$ 5:11   25. $\frac{3}{95}$ 3:92   26. $\frac{9}{70}$ 9:61   27. $\frac{8}{15}$ 8:7

Find the probability of an event occurring, given the odds of the event.

28. 2:23 $\frac{2}{25}$ 29. 2:5 $\frac{2}{7}$ 30. 15:1 $\frac{15}{16}$ 31. 9:7 $\frac{9}{16}$

32. 11:14 $\frac{11}{25}$ 33. 1000:1 $\frac{1000}{1001}$ 34. 12:17 $\frac{12}{29}$ 35. 8:13 $\frac{8}{21}$

© Glencoe/McGraw-Hill 714 Glencoe Algebra 2

Answers

12-3 Reading to Learn Mathematics

Probability

Pre-Activity What do probability and odds tell you about life's risks?

Read the introduction to Lesson 12-3 at the top of page 644 in your textbook.

What is the probability that a person will *not* be struck by lightning in a given year? $\frac{749,999}{750,000}$

Reading the Lesson

1. Indicate whether each of the following statements is *true* or *false*.

a. If an event can never occur, its probability is a negative number. **false**

b. If an event is certain to happen, its probability is 1. **true**

c. If an event can succeed in *s* ways and fail in *f* ways, then the probability of success is $\frac{s}{f}$. **false**

d. If an event can succeed in *s* ways and fail in *f* ways, then the odds against the event are *s:f*. **false**

e. A probability distribution is a function in which the domain is the sample space of an experiment. **true**

2. A weather forecast says that the chance of rain tomorrow is 40%.

a. Write the probability that it will rain tomorrow as a fraction in lowest terms. $\frac{2}{5}$

b. Write the probability that it will not rain tomorrow as a fraction in lowest terms. $\frac{3}{5}$

c. What are the odds in favor of rain? **2:3**

d. What are the odds against rain? **3:2**

3. Refer to the table in Example 4 on page 646 in your textbook.

a. What other sum has the same probability as a sum of 11? **3**

b. What are the odds of rolling a sum of 8? **5:31**

c. What are the odds against rolling a sum of 9? **8:1**

Helping You Remember

4. A good way to remember something is to explain it to someone else. Suppose that your friend Roberto is having trouble remembering the difference between probability and odds. What would you tell him to help him remember this easily?

Sample answer: Probability gives the ratio of successes to the total number of outcomes, while odds gives the ratio of successes to failures.

715

Glencoe Algebra 2

Lesson 12-3

12-3 Enrichment

Geometric Probability

If a dart, thrown at random, hits the triangular board shown at the right, what is the chance that it will hit the shaded region? This chance, also called a probability, can be determined by comparing the area of the shaded region to the area of the board. This ratio indicates what fraction of the tosses should hit in the shaded region.

$$\frac{\text{area of shaded region}}{\text{area of triangular board}} = \frac{\frac{1}{2}(4)(6)}{\frac{1}{2}(8)(6)}$$

$$= \frac{12}{24} \text{ or } \frac{1}{2}$$

In general, if S is a subregion of some region R, then the probability, $P(S)$, that a point, chosen at random, belongs to subregion S is given by the following.

$$P(S) = \frac{\text{area of subregion } S}{\text{are of region } R}$$

Find the probability that a point, chosen at random, belongs to the shaded subregions of the following regions.

1.  $\frac{1}{2}$

2.  $\frac{5}{9}$

3. $\frac{\pi}{4}$

The dart board shown at the right has 5 concentric circles whose centers are also the center of the square board. Each side of the board is 38 cm, and the radii of the circles are 2 cm, 5 cm, 8 cm, 11 cm, and 14 cm. A dart hitting within one of the circular regions scores the number of points indicated on the board, while a hit anywhere else scores 0 points. If a dart, thrown at random, hits the board, find the probability of scoring the indicated number of points.

4. 0 points $\frac{361 - 49\pi}{361}$

5. 1 point $\frac{75\pi}{1444}$

6. 2 points $\frac{57\pi}{1444}$

7. 3 points $\frac{39\pi}{1444}$

8. 4 points $\frac{21\pi}{1444}$

9. 5 points $\frac{\pi}{361}$

716

Glencoe Algebra 2

NAME _____ DATE _____ PERIOD _____

12-4 Study Guide and Intervention

Multiplying Probabilities

Probability of Independent Events

Probability of Two Independent Events	If two events, A and B, are independent, then the probability of both occurring is $P(A \text{ and } B) = P(A) \cdot P(B)$.

Example In a board game each player has 3 different-colored markers. To move around the board the player first spins a spinner to determine which piece can be moved. He or she then rolls a die to determine how many spaces that colored piece should move. On a given turn what is the probability that a player will be able to move the yellow piece more than 2 spaces?

Let A be the event that the spinner lands on yellow, and let B be the event that the die shows a number greater than 2. The probability of A is $\frac{1}{3}$, and the probability of B is $\frac{2}{3}$.

$P(A \text{ and } B) = P(A) \cdot P(B)$ Probability of independent events

$= \frac{1}{3} \cdot \frac{2}{3}$ or $\frac{2}{9}$ Substitute and multiply.

The probability that the player can move the yellow piece more than 2 spaces is $\frac{2}{9}$.

Exercises

A die is rolled 3 times. Find the probability of each event.

1. a 1 is rolled, then a 2, then a 3 $\frac{1}{216}$

2. a 1 or a 2 is rolled, then a 3, then a 5 or a 6 $\frac{1}{54}$

3. 2 odd numbers are rolled, then a 6 $\frac{1}{24}$

4. a number less than 3 is rolled, then a 3, then a number greater than 3 $\frac{1}{36}$

5. A box contains 5 triangles, 6 circles, and 4 squares. If a figure is removed, replaced, and a second figure is picked, what is the probability that a triangle and then a circle will be picked? $\frac{2}{15}$ or about 0.13

6. A bag contains 5 red marbles and 4 white marbles. A marble is selected from the bag, then replaced, and a second selection is made. What is the probability of selecting 2 red marbles? $\frac{25}{81}$ or about 0.31

7. A jar contains 7 lemon jawbreakers, 3 cherry jawbreakers, and 8 rainbow jawbreakers. What is the probability of selecting 2 lemon jawbreakers in succession providing the jawbreaker drawn first is then replaced before the second is drawn? $\frac{49}{324}$ or about 0.15

Lesson 12-4

NAME _____ DATE _____ PERIOD _____

12-4 Study Guide and Intervention (continued)

Multiplying Probabilities

Probability of Dependent Events

Probability of Two Dependent Events	If two events, A and B, are dependent, then the probability of both events occurring is $P(A \text{ and } B) = P(A) \cdot P(B \text{ following } A)$.

Example 1 There are 7 dimes and 9 pennies in a wallet. Suppose two coins are to be selected at random, without replacing the first one. Find the probability of picking a penny and then a dime.

Because the coin is not replaced, the events are dependent.

Thus, $P(A \text{ and } B) = P(A) \cdot P(B \text{ following } A)$.

$P(\text{penny, then dime}) = P(\text{penny}) \cdot P(\text{dime following penny})$

$\frac{9}{16} \cdot \frac{7}{15} = \frac{21}{80}$

The probability is $\frac{21}{80}$ or about 0.26.

Example 2 What is the probability of drawing, without replacement, 3 hearts, then a spade from a standard deck of cards?

Since the cards are not replaced, the events are dependent. Let H represent a heart and S represent a spade.

$P(\text{H, H, H, S}) = P(\text{H}) \cdot P(\text{H following H}) \cdot P(\text{H following 2 Hs}) \cdot P(\text{S following 3 Hs})$

$= \frac{13}{52} \cdot \frac{12}{51} \cdot \frac{11}{50} \cdot \frac{13}{49}$ or about 0.003

The probability is about 0.003 of drawing 3 hearts, then a spade.

Exercises

Find each probability.

1. The cup on Sophie's desk holds 4 red pens and 7 black pens. What is the probability of her selecting first a black pen, then a red one? $\frac{14}{55}$ or about 0.25

2. What is the probability of drawing two cards showing odd numbers from a set of cards that show the first 20 counting numbers if the first card is not replaced before the second is chosen? $\frac{9}{38}$ or about 0.24

3. There are 3 quarters, 4 dimes, and 7 nickels in a change purse. Suppose 3 coins are selected without replacement. What is the probability of selecting a quarter, then a dime, and then a nickel? $\frac{1}{26}$ or about 0.04

4. A basket contains 4 plums, 6 peaches, and 5 oranges. What is the probability of picking 2 oranges, then a peach if 3 pieces of fruit are selected at random? $\frac{4}{91}$ or about 0.04

5. A photographer has taken 8 black and white photographs and 10 color photographs for a brochure. If 4 photographs are selected at random, what is the probability of picking first 2 black and white photographs, then 2 color photographs? $\frac{7}{102}$ or about 0.07

Answers

Skills Practice (left page)

12-4 Skills Practice

Multiplying Probabilities

A die is rolled twice. Find each probability.

1. $P(5, \text{then } 6)$ $\frac{1}{36}$

2. $P(\text{no } 2s)$ $\frac{25}{36}$

3. $P(\text{two } 1s)$ $\frac{1}{36}$

4. $P(\text{any number, then not } 5)$ $\frac{5}{6}$

5. $P(4, \text{then not } 6)$ $\frac{5}{36}$

6. $P(\text{not } 1, \text{then not } 2)$ $\frac{25}{36}$

A board game uses a set of 6 different cards. Each card displays one of the following figures: a star, a square, a circle, a diamond, a rectangle, or a pentagon. The cards are placed face down, and a player chooses two cards. Find each probability.

7. $P(\text{circle, then star})$, if no replacement occurs $\frac{1}{30}$

8. $P(\text{diamond, then square})$, if replacement occurs $\frac{1}{36}$

9. $P(2 \text{ polygons})$, if replacement occurs $\frac{25}{36}$

10. $P(2 \text{ polygons})$, if no replacement occurs $\frac{2}{3}$

11. $P(\text{circle, then hexagon})$, if no replacement occurs 0

Determine whether the events are *independent* or *dependent*. Then find each probability.

12. A mixed box of herbal teabags contains 2 lemon teabags, 3 orange-mango teabags, 3 chamomile teabags, and 1 apricot-ginger teabag. Kevin chooses 2 teabags at random to bring to work with him. What is the probability that he first chooses a lemon teabag and then a chamomile teabag? **dependent;** $\frac{1}{12}$

13. The chart shows the selection of olive oils that Hasha finds in a specialty foods catalog. If she randomly selects one type of oil, then randomly selects another, different oil, what is the probability that both selections are domestic, first cold pressed oils? **dependent;** $\frac{21}{820}$

Type of Oil	Domestic	Imported
Pure	2	5
Cold Pressed	4	8
First Cold Pressed	7	15

For Exercises 14 and 15, two thirds of the area of the spinner earns you 50 points. Suppose you spin the spinner twice.

14. Sketch a tree diagram showing all of the possibilities. Use it to find the probability of spinning 50 points, then 100 points. $\frac{2}{9}$

15. What is the probability that you get 100 points on each spin? $\frac{1}{9}$

Practice (right page)

12-4 Practice (Average)

Multiplying Probabilities

A die is rolled three times. Find each probability.

1. $P(\text{three } 4s)$ $\frac{1}{216}$

2. $P(\text{no } 4s)$ $\frac{125}{216}$

3. $P(2, \text{then } 3, \text{then } 1)$ $\frac{1}{216}$

4. $P(\text{three different even numbers})$ $\frac{1}{36}$

5. $P(\text{any number, then } 5, \text{then } 5)$ $\frac{1}{36}$

6. $P(\text{even number, then odd number, then } 1)$ $\frac{1}{24}$

There are 3 nickels, 2 dimes, and 5 quarters in a purse. Three coins are selected in succession at random. Find the probability.

7. $P(\text{nickel, then dime, then quarter})$, if no replacement occurs $\frac{1}{24}$

8. $P(\text{nickel, then dime, then quarter})$, if replacement occurs $\frac{3}{100}$

9. $P(2 \text{ nickels, then } 1 \text{ quarter})$, if no replacement occurs $\frac{1}{24}$

10. $P(3 \text{ dimes})$, if replacement occurs $\frac{1}{125}$

11. $P(3 \text{ dimes})$, if no replacement occurs 0

For Exercises 12 and 13, determine whether the events are *independent* or *dependent*. Then find each probability.

12. Serena is creating a painting. She wants to use 2 more colors. She chooses randomly from 6 shades of red, 10 shades of green, 4 shades of yellow, 4 shades of purple, and 6 shades of blue. What is the probability that she chooses 2 shades of green? **dependent;** $\frac{3}{29}$

13. Kershel's mother is shopping at a bakery. The owner offers Kershel a cookie from a jar containing 22 chocolate chip cookies, 18 sugar cookies, and 15 oatmeal cookies. Without looking, Kershel selects one, drops it back in, and then randomly selects another. What is the probability that neither selection was a chocolate chip cookie? **independent;** $\frac{9}{25}$

14. METEOROLOGY The Fadeeva's are planning a 3-day vacation to the mountains. A long-range forecast reports that the probability of rain each day is 10%. Assuming that the daily probabilities of rain are independent, what is the probability that there is no rain on the first two days, but that it rains on the third day? $\frac{81}{1000}$

RANDOM NUMBERS For Exercises 15 and 16, use the following information.

Anita has a list of 20 jobs around the house to do, and plans to do 3 of them today. She assigns each job a number from 1 to 20, and sets her calculator to generate random numbers from 1 to 20, which can reoccur. Of the jobs, 3 are outside, and the rest are inside.

15. Sketch a tree diagram showing all of the possibilities that the first three numbers generated correspond to inside jobs or outside jobs. Use it to find the probability that the first two numbers correspond to inside jobs, and the third to an outside job. **0.108375**

16. What is the probability that the number generated corresponds to an outside job three times in a row? **0.003375**

12-4 Reading to Learn Mathematics

Multiplying Probabilities

Pre-Activity **How does probability apply to basketball?**

Read the introduction to Lesson 12-4 at the top of page 651 in your textbook.

Write the probability that Reggie Miller made a free-throw shot during the 1998–99 season as a fraction in lowest terms. (Your answer should not include a decimal.) $\dfrac{183}{200}$

Reading the Lesson

1. A bag contains 4 yellow balls, 5 red balls, 1 white ball, and 2 black balls. A ball is drawn from the bag and is not replaced. A second ball is drawn.

a. Let Y be the event "first ball is yellow" and B be the event "second ball is black." Are these events *independent* or *dependent*? **dependent**

b. Tell which formula you would use to find the probability that the first ball is yellow and the second ball is black. **C**

A. $P(Y \text{ and } B) = \dfrac{P(Y)}{P(Y) + P(B)}$

B. $P(Y \text{ and } B) = P(Y) \cdot P(B)$

C. $P(Y \text{ and } B) = P(Y) \cdot P(B \text{ following } Y)$

c. Which equation shows the correct calculation of this probability? **B**

A. $\dfrac{1}{3} + \dfrac{2}{11} = \dfrac{17}{33}$ B. $\dfrac{1}{3} \cdot \dfrac{2}{11} = \dfrac{2}{33}$

C. $\dfrac{1}{3} \cdot \dfrac{1}{6} = \dfrac{1}{2}$ D. $\dfrac{1}{3} \cdot \dfrac{1}{6} = \dfrac{1}{18}$

d. Which equation shows the correct calculation of the probability that if three balls are drawn in succession without replacement, all three will be red? **B**

A. $\dfrac{5}{12} \cdot \dfrac{5}{12} \cdot \dfrac{5}{12} = \dfrac{125}{1728}$ B. $\dfrac{5}{12} \cdot \dfrac{4}{11} \cdot \dfrac{3}{10} = \dfrac{1}{22}$

C. $\dfrac{5}{12} + \dfrac{4}{11} + \dfrac{3}{10} = \dfrac{713}{660}$

Helping You Remember

2. Some students have trouble remembering a lot of formulas, so they try to keep the number of formulas they have to know to a minimum. Can you learn just one formula that will allow you to find probabilities for both independent and dependent events? Explain your reasoning. **Sample answer: Just remember the formula for dependent events:** $P(A \text{ and } B) = P(A) \cdot P(B \text{ following } A)$. **When the events are independent,** $P(B \text{ following } A) = P(B)$, **so the formula for dependent events simplifies to** $P(A \text{ and } B) = P(A) \cdot P(B)$, **which is the correct formula for independent events.**

12-4 Enrichment

Conditional Probability

Suppose a pair of dice is thrown. It is known that the sum is greater than seven. Find the probability that the dice match.

The probability of an event given the occurrence of another event is called *conditional probability*. The conditional probability of event A, the dice match, given event B, their sum is greater than seven, is denoted $P(A/B)$.

There are 15 sums greater than seven and there are 36 possible pairs altogether.

$P(B) = \dfrac{15}{36}$

There are three matching pairs greater than seven.

$P(A \text{ and } B) = \dfrac{3}{36}$

$P(A/B) = \dfrac{P(A \text{ and } B)}{P(B)}$

$P(A/B) = \dfrac{\frac{3}{36}}{\frac{15}{36}} \text{ or } \dfrac{1}{5}$

The conditional probability is $\dfrac{1}{5}$.

A card is drawn from a standard deck of 52 and is found to be red. Given that event, find each of the following probabilities.

1. $P(\text{heart})$ $\dfrac{1}{2}$ 2. $P(\text{ace})$ $\dfrac{1}{13}$ 3. $P(\text{face card})$ $\dfrac{3}{13}$

4. $P(\text{jack or ten})$ $\dfrac{2}{13}$ 5. $P(\text{six of spades})$ 0 6. $P(\text{six of hearts})$ $\dfrac{1}{26}$

A sports survey taken at Stirers High School shows that 48% of the respondents liked soccer, 66% liked basketball, and 38% liked hockey. Also, 30% liked soccer and basketball, 22% liked basketball and hockey and 28% liked soccer and hockey. Finally, 12% liked all three sports. Find each of the following probabilities.

7. The probability Meg likes soccer if she likes basketball. $\dfrac{30}{66} \text{ or } \dfrac{5}{11}$

8. The probability Biff likes basketball if he likes soccer. $\dfrac{30}{48} \text{ or } \dfrac{5}{8}$

9. The probability Muffy likes hockey if she likes basketball. $\dfrac{22}{66} \text{ or } \dfrac{1}{3}$

10. The probability Greg likes hockey and basketball if he likes soccer. $\dfrac{12}{48} \text{ or } \dfrac{1}{4}$

Lesson 12-4

Answers

12-5 Study Guide and Intervention

Adding Probabilities

Mutually Exclusive Events Events that cannot occur at the same time are called mutually exclusive events.

Probability of Mutually Exclusive Events	If two events, A and B, are mutually exclusive, then $P(A \text{ or } B) = P(A) + P(B)$.

This formula can be extended to any number of mutually exclusive events.

Example 1 **To choose an afternoon activity, summer campers pull slips of paper out of a hat. Today there are 25 slips for a nature walk, 35 slips for swimming, and 30 slips for arts and crafts. What is the probability that a camper will pull a slip for a nature walk or for swimming?**

These are mutually exclusive events. Note that there is a total of 90 slips.

$P(\text{nature walk or swimming}) = P(\text{nature walk}) + P(\text{swimming})$

$= \dfrac{25}{90} + \dfrac{35}{90}$ or $\dfrac{2}{3}$

The probability of a camper's pulling out a slip for a nature walk or for swimming is $\dfrac{2}{3}$.

Example 2 **By the time one tent of 6 campers gets to the front of the line, there are only 10 nature walk slips and 15 swimming slips left. What is the probability that more than 4 of the 6 campers will choose a swimming slip?**

$P(\text{more than 4 swimmers}) = P(5 \text{ swimmers}) + P(6 \text{ swimmers})$

$= \dfrac{C(10, 1) \cdot C(15, 5)}{C(25, 6)} + \dfrac{C(10, 0) \cdot C(15, 6)}{C(25, 6)}$

≈ 0.2

The probability of more than 4 of the campers swimming is about 0.2.

Exercises

Find each probability.

1. A bag contains 45 dyed eggs: 15 yellow, 12 green, and 18 red. What is the probability of selecting a green or a red egg? $\dfrac{2}{3}$

2. The letters from the words LOVE and LIVE are placed on cards and put in a box. What is the probability of selecting an L or an O from the box? $\dfrac{3}{8}$

3. A pair of dice is rolled, and the two numbers are added. What is the probability that the sum is either a 5 or a 7? $\dfrac{5}{18}$ or about 0.28

4. A bowl has 10 whole wheat crackers, 16 sesame crackers, and 14 rye crisps. If a person picks a cracker at random, what is the probability of picking either a sesame cracker or a rye crisp? $\dfrac{3}{4}$

5. An art box contains 12 colored pencils and 20 pastels. If 5 drawing implements are chosen at random, what is the probability that at least 4 of them are pastels? about 0.37

© Glencoe/McGraw-Hill   723   *Glencoe Algebra 2*

12-5 Study Guide and Intervention *(continued)*

Adding Probabilities

Inclusive Events

Probability of Inclusive Events	If two events, A and B, are inclusive, $P(A \text{ or } B) = P(A) + P(B) - P(A \text{ and } B)$.

Example **What is the probability of drawing a face card or a black card from a standard deck of cards?**

The two events are inclusive, since a card can be both a face card and a black card.

$P(\text{face card or black card}) = P(\text{face card}) + P(\text{black card}) - P(\text{black face card})$

$= \dfrac{3}{13} + \dfrac{1}{2} - \dfrac{3}{26}$

$= \dfrac{8}{13}$ or about 0.62

The probability of drawing either a face card or a black card is about 0.62.

Exercises

Find each probability.

1. What is the probability of drawing a red card or an ace from a standard deck of cards? $\dfrac{7}{13}$ or about 0.54

2. Three cards are selected from a standard deck of 52 cards. What is the probability of selecting a king, a queen, or a red card? $\dfrac{15}{26}$ or about 0.58

3. The letters of the alphabet are placed in a bag. What is the probability of selecting a vowel or one of the letters from the word QUIZ? $\dfrac{7}{26}$ or about 0.27

4. A pair of dice is rolled. What is the probability that the sum is odd or a multiple of 3? $\dfrac{2}{3}$ or about 0.67

5. The Venn diagram at the right shows the number of juniors on varsity sports teams at Elmwood High School. Some athletes are on varsity teams for one season only, some athletes for two seasons, and some for all three seasons. If a varsity athlete is chosen at random from the junior class, what is the probability that he or she plays a fall or winter sport? $\dfrac{13}{16}$

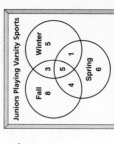

Juniors Playing Varsity Sports

Fall 8 — 3 — Winter 5
5
4 — 1
Spring 6

© Glencoe/McGraw-Hill   724   *Glencoe Algebra 2*

NAME _____ DATE _____ PERIOD _____

12-5 Skills Practice
Adding Probabilities

Eli has 10 baseball cards of 10 different players in his pocket. Three players are pitchers, 5 are outfielders, and 2 are catchers. If Eli randomly selects a card to trade, find each probability.

1. P(pitcher or outfielder) $\frac{4}{5}$ 2. P(pitcher or catcher) $\frac{1}{2}$ 3. P(outfielder or catcher) $\frac{7}{10}$

A die is rolled. Find each probability.

4. P(5 or 6) $\frac{1}{3}$ 5. P(at least a 3) $\frac{2}{3}$ 6. P(less than 4) $\frac{1}{2}$

Determine whether the events are *mutually exclusive* or *inclusive*. Then find the probability.

7. A die is rolled. What is the probability of rolling a 3 or a 4? mutually exclusive; $\frac{1}{3}$

8. A die is rolled. What is the probability of rolling an even number or a 4? inclusive; $\frac{1}{2}$

9. A card is drawn from a standard deck of cards. What is the probability of drawing a king or a queen? mutually exclusive; $\frac{2}{13}$

10. A card is drawn from a standard deck of cards. What is the probability of drawing a jack or a heart? inclusive; $\frac{4}{13}$

11. The sophomore class is selling Mother's Day plants to raise money. Susan's prize for being the top seller of plants is a choice of a book, a CD, or a video. She can choose from 6 books, 3 CDs, and 5 videos. What is the probability that Susan selects a book or a CD? mutually exclusive; $\frac{9}{14}$

A spinner numbered 1–10 is spun. Find each probability.

12. P(less than 5 or even) $\frac{7}{10}$ 13. P(even or odd) 1   14. P(prime or even) $\frac{4}{5}$

Two cards are drawn from a standard deck of cards. Find each probability.

15. P(both red or both black) $\frac{25}{51}$ 16. P(both aces or both red) $\frac{55}{221}$
17. P(both 2s or both less than 5) $\frac{11}{221}$ 18. P(both black or both less than 5) $\frac{188}{663}$

For Exercises 19 and 20, use the Venn diagram that shows the number of participants in two kinds of aerobic exercise classes that are offered at a health club. Determine each probability if a person is selected at random from the participants.

Venn diagram: Step Aerobics 22, 13, Jazzercise 27

19. P(step aerobics or jazzercise, but not both) $\frac{49}{62}$

20. P(step aerobics and jazzercise) $\frac{13}{62}$

© Glencoe/McGraw-Hill   725   *Glencoe Algebra 2*

NAME _____ DATE _____ PERIOD _____

12-5 Practice (Average)
Adding Probabilities

An urn contains 7 white marbles and 5 blue marbles. Four marbles are selected without replacement. Find each probability.

1. P(4 white or 4 blue) $\frac{8}{99}$ 2. P(exactly 3 white) $\frac{35}{99}$ 3. P(at least 3 white) $\frac{14}{33}$

4. P(fewer than 3 white) $\frac{19}{33}$ 5. P(3 white or 3 blue) $\frac{49}{99}$ 6. P(no white or no blue) $\frac{8}{99}$

Jason and Maria are playing a board game in which three dice are tossed to determine a player's move. Find each probability.

7. P(two 5s) $\frac{5}{72}$ 8. P(three 5s) $\frac{1}{216}$ 9. P(at least two 5s) $\frac{2}{27}$

10. P(no 5s) $\frac{125}{216}$ 11. P(one 5) $\frac{25}{72}$ 12. P(one 5 or two 5s) $\frac{5}{12}$

Determine whether the events are *mutually exclusive* or *inclusive*. Then find the probability.

13. A clerk chooses 4 CD players at random for floor displays from a shipment of 24 CD players. If 15 of the players have a blue case and the rest have a red case, what is the probability of choosing 4 players with a blue case or 4 players with a red case? mutual. exclus.; $\frac{71}{506}$

14. A department store employs 28 high school students, all juniors and seniors. Six of the 12 seniors are females and 12 of the juniors are males. One student employee is chosen at random. What is the probability of selecting a senior or a female? inclusive; $\frac{4}{7}$

15. A restaurant has 5 pieces of apple pie, 4 pieces of chocolate cream pie, and 3 pieces of blueberry pie. If Janine selects a piece of pie at random for dessert, what is the probability that she selects either apple or chocolate cream? mutually exclusive; $\frac{3}{4}$

16. At a statewide meeting, there are 20 school superintendents, 13 principals, and 6 assistant principals. If one of these people is chosen at random, what is the probability that he or she is either a principal or an assistant principal? mutually exclusive; $\frac{19}{39}$

17. An airline has one bank of 13 telephones at a reservations office. Of the 13 operators who work there, 8 take reservations for domestic flights and 5 take reservations for international flights. Seven of the operators taking domestic reservations and 3 of the operators taking international reservations are female. If an operator is chosen at random, what is the probability that the person chosen takes domestic reservations or is a male? inclusive; $\frac{10}{13}$

18. MUSIC Forty senior citizens were surveyed about their music preferences. The results are displayed in the Venn diagram. If a senior citizen from the survey group is selected at random, what is the probability that he or she likes only country and western music? What is the probability that he or she likes classical and/or country, but not 1940's pop? $\frac{3}{20}; \frac{2}{5}$

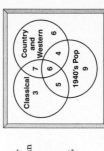

Venn diagram: Classical 3, 7, Country and Western 6, 6, 4, 5, 1940's Pop 9

© Glencoe/McGraw-Hill   726   *Glencoe Algebra 2*

12-5 Reading to Learn Mathematics

Adding Probabilities

Pre-Activity How does probability apply to your personal habits?

Read the introduction to Lesson 12-5 at the top of page 658 in your textbook.

Why do the percentages shown on the bar graph add up to more than 100%? **Sample answer: Many people do more than one of the listed bedtime rituals.**

Reading the Lesson

1. Indicate whether the events in each pair are *inclusive* or *mutually exclusive.*

   a. *Q*: drawing a queen from a standard deck of cards
      D: drawing a diamond from a standard deck of cards **inclusive**

   b. *J*: drawing a jack from a standard deck of cards
      K: drawing a king from a standard deck of cards **mutually exclusive**

2. Marla took a quiz on this lesson that contained the following problem.
   Each of the integers from 1 through 25 is written on a slip of paper and placed in an envelope. If one slip is drawn at random, what is the probability that it is odd or a multiple of 5?

   Here is Marla's work.

   $P(\text{odd}) = \dfrac{13}{25}$ $P(\text{multiple of 5}) = \dfrac{5}{25} \text{ or } \dfrac{1}{5}$

   $P(\text{odd or multiple of 5}) = P(\text{odd}) + P(\text{multiple of 5})$

   $= \dfrac{13}{25} + \dfrac{5}{25} = \dfrac{18}{25}$

   a. Why is Marla's work incorrect? **Sample answer: Marla used the formula for mutually exclusive events, but the events are inclusive. She should use the formula for inclusive events so that the odd multiples of 5 will not be counted twice.**

   b. Show the corrected work.

   $P(\text{odd or multiple of 5}) = P(\text{odd}) + P(\text{multiple of 5}) - P(\text{odd multiple of 5})$

   $= \dfrac{13}{25} + \dfrac{5}{25} - \dfrac{3}{25} = \dfrac{15}{25} = \dfrac{3}{5}$

Helping You Remember

3. Some students have trouble remembering a lot of formulas, so they try to keep the number of formulas they have to know to a minimum. Can you learn just one formula that will allow you to find probabilities for both mutually exclusive and inclusive events? Explain your reasoning. **Sample answer: Just remember the formula for inclusive events:** $P(A \text{ or } B) = P(A) + P(B) - P(A \text{ and } B)$. **When the events are mutually exclusive,** $P(A \text{ and } B) = 0$, **so the formula for inclusive events simplifies to** $P(A \text{ and } B) = P(A) + P(B)$, **which is the correct formula for mutually exclusive events.**

12-5 Enrichment

Probability and Tic-Tac-Toe

What would be the chances of winning at tic-tac-toe if it were turned into a game of pure chance? To find out, the nine cells of the tic-tac-toe board are numbered from 1 to 9 and nine chips (also numbered from 1 to 9) are put into a bag. Player A draws a chip at random and enters an *X* in the corresponding cell. Player B draws the same and enters an *O*.

To solve the problem, assume that both players draw all their chips without looking and all *X* and *O* entries are made at the same time. There are four possible outcomes: a draw, A wins, B wins, and either A or B can win.

There are 16 arrangements that result in a draw. Reflections and rotations must be counted as shown below.

```
X O X    X O X    O O X
O O X    O O X    X X O 8
X O X    X X O    O X X
```

There are 36 arrangements in which either player may win because both players have winning triples.

```
X X X    X X X    X O X    X X X    X X X
O O O 4  X O X 4  X X X 4  X X O 8  O O O 8  X X X 8
X O X    O O O    O O O    O O O    X X O    O O O
```

In these 36 cases, A's chances of winning are $\dfrac{13}{40}$.

1. Find the 12 arrangements in which B wins and A cannot.

```
O O X    O X O
X O X 8  X O X 4
X X O    X X O
```

2. Below are 12 of the arrangements in which A wins and B cannot. Write the numbers to show the reflections and rotations for each arrangement. What is the total number? **62**

```
O X O    X O X    X X X    X X X    X O O    X O O 4
X X X 1  O X O X  X O O 4  O X O 4  X X X 4  X X O 4
O X O    X O X    X O O    O X O    O O X    O O X

X X O    X X X    X X X    X O O    X O O 8  X X O
O O X 4  O X O 8  X O O 8  X X X 8  X X O 8  O X O 8
O O X    X X O    O O O    O O O    O X O    X O X
```

3. There are $\dfrac{9!}{(5!4!)}$ different and equally probable distributions. Complete the chart to find the probability for a draw or for A or B to win.

Draw:	$\dfrac{16}{126}$		$= \dfrac{8}{63}$	
A wins:	$\dfrac{62}{126}$	$+ \ 13\left(\dfrac{36}{40}\right)\left(\dfrac{1}{126}\right)$	$= \dfrac{737}{1260}$	
B wins:	$\dfrac{12}{126}$	$+ \ 27\left(\dfrac{36}{40}\right)\left(\dfrac{1}{126}\right)$	$= \dfrac{121}{420}$	

NAME _____ DATE _____ PERIOD _____

12-6 Study Guide and Intervention

Statistical Measures

Measures of Central Tendency

Measures of Central Tendency	Use	When
	mean	the data are spread out and you want an average of values
	median	the data contain outliers
	mode	the data are tightly clustered around one or two values

Example **Find the mean, median, and mode of the following set of data:**
{42, 39, 35, 40, 38, 35, 45}.

To find the mean, add the values and divide by the number of values.

mean = $\frac{42 + 39 + 35 + 40 + 38 + 35 + 45}{7} \approx 39.14$.

To find the median, arrange the values in ascending or descending order and choose the middle value. (If there is an even number of values, find the mean of the two middle values.) In this case, the median is 39.

To find the mode, take the most common value. In this case, the mode is 35.

Exercises

Find the mean, median, and mode of each set of data. Round to the nearest hundredth, if necessary.

1. {238, 261, 245, 249, 255, 262, 241, 245} 249.5; 247; 245

2. {9, 13, 8, 10, 11, 9, 12, 16, 10, 9} 10.7; 10; 9

3. {120, 108, 145, 129, 102, 132, 134, 118, 108, 142} 123.8; 124.5; 108

4. {68, 54, 73, 58, 63, 72, 65, 70, 61} 64.89; 65; no mode

5. {34, 49, 42, 38, 40, 45, 34, 28, 43, 30} 38.3; 39; 34

6. The table at the right shows the populations of the six New England capitals. Which would be the most appropriate measure of central tendency to represent the data? Explain why and find that value.
Source: www.factfinder.census.gov **There is no mode. The population of Boston is an outlier and would raise the mean too high. The median, 79,500, would be the best choice.**

City	Population (rounded to the nearest 1000)
Augusta, ME	19,000
Boston, MA	589,000
Concord, NH	37,000
Hartford, CT	122,000
Montpelier, VT	8,000
Providence, RI	174,000

NAME _____ DATE _____ PERIOD _____

12-6 Study Guide and Intervention (continued)

Statistical Measures

Measures of Variation The *range* and the **standard deviation** measure how scattered a set of data is.

Standard Deviation	If a set of data consists of the n values $x_1, x_2, \ldots, x_n$ and has mean $\bar{x}$, then the standard deviation is given by $\sigma = \sqrt{\frac{(x_1 - \bar{x})^2 + (x_2 - \bar{x})^2 + \cdots + (x_n - \bar{x})^2}{n}}$.

The square of the standard deviation is called the **variance.**

Example **Find the variance and standard deviation of the data set {10, 9, 6, 9, 18, 4, 8, 20}.**

Step 1 Find the mean.

$\bar{x} = \frac{10 + 9 + 6 + 9 + 18 + 4 + 8 + 20}{8} = 10.5$

Step 2 Find the variance.

$\sigma^2 = \frac{(x_1 - \bar{x})^2 + (x_2 - \bar{x})^2 + \cdots + (x_n - \bar{x})^2}{n}$ Standard variance formula

$= \frac{(10 - 10.5)^2 + (9 - 10.5)^2 + \cdots + (20 - 10.5)^2}{8}$

$= \frac{220}{8}$ or 27.5

Step 3 Find the standard deviation.

$\sigma = \sqrt{27.5}$

≈ 5.2

The variance is 27.5 and the standard deviation is about 5.2.

Exercises

Find the variance and standard deviation of each set of data. Round to the nearest tenth.

1. {100, 89, 112, 104, 96, 108, 93}
58.5; 7.6

2. {62, 54, 49, 62, 48, 53, 50}
29.4; 5.4

3. {8, 9, 8, 8, 9, 7, 8, 9, 6}
0.9; 0.9

4. {4.2, 5.0, 4.7, 4.5, 5.2, 4.8, 4.6, 5.1}
0.1; 0.3

5. The table at the right lists the prices of ten brands of breakfast cereal. What is the standard deviation of the values to the nearest penny? **$0.33**

Price of 10 Brands of Breakfast Cereal	
$2.29	$3.19
$3.39	$2.79
$2.99	$3.09
$3.19	$2.59
$2.79	$3.29

Answers

Lesson 12-6

Skills Practice (page 731)

NAME _____ DATE _____ PERIOD _____

12-6 Skills Practice
Statistical Measures

Find the variance and standard deviation of each set of data to the nearest tenth.

1. {32, 41, 35, 35, 46, 42} 23.6, 4.9

2. {13, 62, 77, 24, 38, 19, 88} 763.8, 27.6

3. {89, 99, 42, 16, 42, 71, 16} 959.1, 31.0

4. {450, 400, 625, 225, 300, 750, 650, 625} 30,537.1; 174.7

5. {17, 23, 65, 94, 33, 33, 33, 8, 57, 75, 44, 12, 11, 68, 39} 630.7, 25.1

6. {7.2, 2.1, 3.8, 9.5, 8.3, 8.4} 5.8, 2.4

7. {1.5, 2.5, 3.5, 4.5, 4.5, 5.5, 6.5, 7.5} 3.5, 1.9

For Exercises 8 and 9, use the table that shows the profit in billions of dollars reported by U.S. manufacturers for the first quarter of the years from 1997 through 2001.

Year	1997	1998	1999	2000	2001
Seasonally-Adjusted Profit ($ billions)	$61.4	$75.6	$60.9	$78.5	$45.3

Source: U.S. Census Bureau

8. Find the mean and median of the data to the nearest tenth. $64.3 billion, $61.4 billion

9. Which measure of central tendency best represents the data? Explain. **The median is more representative because the value 45.3 is not close to the other data points, and it lowers the mean.**

For Exercises 10 and 11, use the table that shows the percent of fourth grade students reading at or above the proficiency level in a nationally-administered reading assessment.

Year	1992	1994	1998	2000
Percent at or above proficiency level	29%	30%	31%	32%

Source: National Center for Education Statistics

10. Find the mean, median, and standard deviation of the data to the nearest tenth. 30.5%, 30.5%, 1.1%

11. What do the statistics from Exercise 11 tell you about the data? **Sample answer: Since the median and mean are equal and the standard deviation is small, the percent of students reading at or above the proficiency level has not varied much from 1992 to 2000.**

Practice (page 732)

NAME _____ DATE _____ PERIOD _____

12-6 Practice (Average)
Statistical Measures

Find the variance and standard deviation of each set of data to the nearest tenth.

1. {47, 61, 93, 22, 82, 22, 37} 673.1, 25.9

2. {10, 10, 54, 39, 96, 91, 91, 18} 1228.6, 35.1

3. {1, 2, 2, 3, 3, 3, 4, 4, 4, 4, 5, 5, 5, 5} 1.6, 1.2

4. {1100, 725, 850, 335, 700, 800, 950} 49,150.0; 221.7

5. {3.4, 7.1, 8.5, 5.1, 4.7, 6.3, 9.9, 8.4, 3.6} 4.7, 2.2

6. {2.8, 0.5, 1.9, 0.8, 1.9, 1.5, 3.3, 2.6, 0.7, 2.5} 0.8, 0.9

7. **HEALTH CARE** Eight physicians with 15 patients on a hospital floor see these patients an average of 18 minutes a day. The 22 nurses on the same floor see the patients an average of 3 hours a day. As a hospital administrator, would you quote the mean, median, or mode as an indicator of the amount of daily medical attention the patients on this floor receive? Explain. **Either the median or the mode; they are equal and higher than the mean, which is lowered by the smaller amount of time the physicians spend with the patients.**

For Exercises 8–10, use the frequency table that shows the percent of public school teachers in the U.S. in 1999 who used computers or the Internet at school for various administrative and teaching activities.

Activity	Percent Using Computer or Internet
Create instructional materials	39
Administrative record keeping	34
Communicate with colleagues	23
Gather information for planning lessons	16
Multimedia classroom presentations	8
Access research and best practices for teaching	8
Communicate with parents or students	8
Access model lesson plans	6

Source: National Assessment of Educational Progress

8. Find the mean, median, and mode of the data. 17.75%, 12%, 8%

9. Suppose you believe teachers use computers or the Internet too infrequently. Which measure would you quote as the "average?" Explain. **Mode; it is lowest.**

10. Suppose you believe teachers use computers or the Internet too often. Which measure would you quote as the "average?" Explain. **Mean; it is highest.**

For Exercises 11 and 12, use the frequency table that shows the number of games played by 24 American League baseball players between opening day, 2001 and September 8, 2001.

No. of Games	Frequency
141	4
140	3
139	4
138	5
137	2
136	3
135	3

Source: Major League Baseball

11. Find the mean, median, mode, and standard deviation of the number of games played to the nearest tenth. 138.2, 138; 138, 2.0

12. For how many players is the number of games within one standard deviation of the mean? 14

Lesson 12-6

12-6 Reading to Learn Mathematics

Statistical Measures

Pre-Activity **What statistics should a teacher tell the class after a test?**

Read the introduction to Lesson 12-6 at the top of page 664 in your textbook.

There is more than one way to give an "average" score for this test. Three measures of central tendency for these scores are 94, 76.5 and 73.9. Can you tell which of these is the mean, the median, and the mode without doing any calculations? Explain your answer.

Sample answer: Yes. The mode must be one of the scores, so it must be an integer. The median must be either one of the scores or halfway between two of the scores, so it must be an integer or a decimal ending with .5. Therefore, 94 is the mode, 76.5 is the median, and 73.9 is the mean.

Reading the Lesson

1. Match each measure with one of the six descriptions of how to find measures of central tendency and variation.

a. median **vi**   **b.** mode **i**   **c.** range **iv**

d. variance **iii**   **e.** mean **ii**   **f.** standard deviation **v**

i. Find the most commonly occurring values or values in a set of data.

ii. Add the data and divide by the number of items.

iii. Find the mean of the squares of the differences between each value in the set of data and the mean.

iv. Find the difference between the largest and smallest values in the set of data.

v. Take the positive square root of the variance.

vi. If there is an odd number of items in a set of data, take the middle one. If there is an even number of items, add the two middle items and divide by 2.

Helping You Remember

2. It is usually easier to remember a complicated procedure if you break it down into steps. Write the procedure for finding the standard deviation for a set of data in a series of brief, numbered steps.

Sample answer:
1. Find the mean.
2. Find the difference between each value and the mean.
3. Square each difference.
4. Find the mean of the squares.
5. Take the positive square root.

12-6 Enrichment

Probabilities in Genetics

Genes are the units which transmit hereditary traits. The possible forms which a gene may take, **dominant** and **recessive**, are called **alleles**. A particular trait is determined by two alleles, one from the female parent and one from the male parent. If an organism has the trait which is dominant, it may have either two dominant alleles or one dominant and one recessive allele. If the organism has the trait which is recessive, it must have two recessive alleles.

Example   **Consider a plant in which tall stems, T, are dominant to short stems, t. What is the probability of obtaining a long-stemmed plant if two long-stemmed plants both with the genetic formula Tt are crossed?**

A *Punnett square* is a chart used to determine the possible combinations of characteristics among offspring.

	T	t
T	TT	Tt
t	Tt	tt

   3 tall-stemmed
+ 1 short-stemmed
4 total

Thus, the probability is $\frac{3}{4}$.

In a certain plant, red flowers, R, are dominant to white flowers, r. If a white-flowered plant, rr, is crossed with a red-flowered plant, Rr, find the probability of each of the following.

1. white-flowered plant $\frac{1}{2}$ 2. red-flowered plant $\frac{1}{2}$

In a certain plant, tall, T, is dominant to short, t, and green pods, G, are dominant to yellow pods, g. Plants with the genetic formulas $TtGg$ and $TTGg$ are crossed. Find the probability of each of the following.

3. tall plant with green pods $\frac{3}{4}$ 4. tall plant with yellow pods $\frac{1}{4}$

Answers

Left Page

12-7 Study Guide and Intervention

The Normal Distribution

Normal and Skewed Distributions A continuous probability distribution is represented by a curve.

Types of Continuous Distributions	Normal	Positively Skewed	Negatively Skewed

Example Determine whether the data below appear to be *positively skewed, negatively skewed,* or *normally distributed.*
{100, 120, 110, 100, 110, 80, 100, 90, 100, 120, 100, 90, 110, 100, 90, 80, 100, 90}
Make a frequency table for the data.

Value	80	90	100	110	120
Frequency	2	4	7	3	2

Then use the data to make a histogram.
Since the histogram is roughly symmetric, the data appear to be normally distributed.

Exercises

Determine whether the data in each table appear to be *positively skewed, negatively skewed,* or *normally distributed.* **Make a histogram of the data.**

1. {27, 24, 29, 25, 27, 22, 24, 25, 29, 24, 25, 22, 27, 24, 22, 25, 24, 22}
positively skewed

2.

Shoe Size	4	5	6	7	8	9	10
No. of Students	1	2	4	8	5	1	2

normally distributed

3.

Housing Price	No. of Houses Sold
less than $100,000	0
$100,00-$120,000	1
$121,00-$140,000	3
$141,00-$160,000	7
$161,00-$180,000	8
$181,00-$200,000	6
over $200,000	12

negatively skewed

Right Page

12-7 Study Guide and Intervention (continued)

The Normal Distribution

Use Normal Distributions

Normal Distribution Normal distributions have these properties.
The graph is maximized at the mean.
The mean, median, and mode are about equal.
About 68% of the values are within one standard deviation of the mean.
About 95% of the values are within two standard deviations of the mean.
About 99% of the values are within three standard deviations of the mean.

Example The heights of players in a basketball league are normally distributed with a mean of 6 feet 1 inch and a standard deviation of 2 inches.

a. What is the probability that a player selected at random will be shorter than 5 feet 9 inches?
Draw a normal curve. Label the mean and the mean plus or minus multiples of the standard deviation.
The value of 5 feet 9 inches is 2 standard deviations below the mean, so approximately 2.5% of the players will be shorter than 5 feet 9 inches.

b. If there are 240 players in the league, about how many players are taller than 6 feet 3 inches?
The value of 6 feet 3 inches is one standard deviation above the mean. Approximately 16% of the players will be taller than this height.
$240 \times 0.16 \approx 38$
About 38 of the players are taller than 6 feet 3 inches.

Exercises

EGG PRODUCTION The number of eggs laid per year by a particular breed of chicken is normally distributed with a mean of 225 and a standard deviation of 10 eggs.

1. About what percent of the chickens will lay between 215 and 235 eggs per year? **68%**

2. In a flock of 400 chickens, about how many would you expect to lay more than 245 eggs per year? **10 chickens**

MANUFACTURING The diameter of bolts produced by a manufacturing plant is normally distributed with a mean of 18 mm and a standard deviation of 0.2 mm.

3. What percent of bolts coming off of the assembly line have a diameter greater than 18.4 mm? **2.5%**

4. What percent have a diameter between 17.8 and 18.2 mm? **68%**

Skills Practice (left page)

12-7 Skills Practice
The Normal Distribution

Determine whether the data in each table appear to be *positively skewed, negatively skewed, or normally distributed.*

1.
Miles Run	Track Team Members
0-4	3
5-9	4
10-14	7
15-19	5
20-23	2

normally distributed

2.
Speeches Given	Political Candidates
0-5	1
6-11	2
12-17	3
18-23	8
24-29	8

positively skewed

For Exercises 3 and 4, use the frequency table that shows the average number of days patients spent on the surgical ward of a hospital last year.

Days	Number of Patients
0-3	5
4-7	18
8-11	11
12-15	9
16+	6

3. Make a histogram of the data.

4. Do the data appear to be *positively skewed, negatively skewed, or normally distributed?* Explain. **Positively skewed; the histogram is high at the left and has a tail to the right.**

DELIVERY For Exercises 5–7, use the following information.
The time it takes a bicycle courier to deliver a parcel to his farthest customer is normally distributed with a mean of 40 minutes and a standard deviation of 4 minutes.

5. About what percent of the courier's trips to this customer take between 36 and 44 minutes? **68%**

6. About what percent of the courier's trips to this customer take between 40 and 48 minutes? **47.5%**

7. About what percent of the courier's trips to this customer take less than 32 minutes? **2.5%**

TESTING For Exercises 8–10, use the following information.
The average time it takes sophomores to complete a math test is normally distributed with a mean of 63.3 minutes and a standard deviation of 12.3 minutes.

8. About what percent of the sophomores take more than 75.6 minutes to complete the test? **16%**

9. About what percent of the sophomores take between 51 and 63.3 minutes? **34%**

10. About what percent of the sophomores take less than 63.3 minutes to complete the test? **50%**

Practice (Average) (right page)

12-7 Practice (Average)
The Normal Distribution

Determine whether the data in each table appear to be *positively skewed, negatively skewed, or normally distributed.*

1.
Time Spent at a Museum Exhibit	
Minutes	Frequency
0-25	27
26-50	46
51-75	89
75-100	57
100+	24

normally distributed

2.
Average Age of High School Principals	
Age in Years	Number
31-35	3
36-40	8
41-45	15
46-50	32
51-55	40
56-60	38
60+	4

negatively skewed

For Exercises 3 and 4, use the frequency table that shows the number of hours worked per week by 100 high school seniors.

Hours	Number of Students
0-8	30
9-17	45
18-25	20
26+	5

3. Make a histogram of the data.

4. Do the data appear to be *positively skewed, negatively skewed, or normally distributed?* Explain. **Positively skewed; the histogram is high at the left and has a tail to the right.**

TESTING For Exercises 5–10, use the following information.
The scores on a test administered to prospective employees are normally distributed with a mean of 100 and a standard deviation of 15.

5. About what percent of the scores are between 70 and 130? **95%**

6. About what percent of the scores are between 85 and 130? **81.5%**

7. About what percent of the scores are over 115? **16%**

8. About what percent of the scores are lower than 85 or higher than 115? **32%**

9. If 80 people take the test, how many would you expect to score higher than 130? **2**

10. If 75 people take the test, how many would you expect to score lower than 85? **12**

11. **TEMPERATURE** The daily July surface temperature of a lake at a resort has a mean of 82° and a standard deviation of 4.2°. If you prefer to swim when the temperature is at least 77.8°, about what percent of the days does the temperature meet your preference? **84%**

12-7 Reading to Learn Mathematics

The Normal Distribution

Pre-Activity **How are the heights of professional athletes distributed?**

Read the introduction to Lesson 12-7 at the top of page 671 in your textbook.
There were 53 players on the team and the mean height was approximately 73.6. About what fraction of the players' heights are between 72 and 75, inclusive? **Sample answer: about $\frac{2}{3}$**

Reading the Lesson

1. Indicate whether each of the following statements is *true* or *false.*

   a. In a continuous probability distribution, there is a finite number of possible outcomes. **false**

   b. Every normal distribution can be represented by a bell curve. **true**

   c. A distribution that is represented by a curve that is high at the left and has a tail to the right is negatively skewed. **false**

   d. A normal distribution is an example of a skewed distribution. **false**

2. Ms. Rose gave the same quiz to her two geometry classes. She recorded the following scores.

First-period class:

Score	0	1	2	3	4	5	6	7	8	9	10
Frequency	1	0	1	0	3	4	5	7	4	3	2

Fifth-period class:

Score	0	1	2	3	4	5	6	7	8	9	10
Frequency	0	0	0	0	3	4	9	7	6	1	0

In each class, 30 students took the quiz. The mean score for each class was 6.4. Which set of scores has the greater standard deviation? (Answer this question without doing any calculations.) Explain your answer.

First period class; sample answer: The scores are more spread out from the mean than for the fifth period class.

Helping You Remember

3. Many students have trouble remembering how to determine if a curve represents a distribution that is *positively skewed* or *negatively skewed.* What is an easy way to remember this?

   Sample answer: Follow the tail! If the tail is on the right (positive direction), the distribution is positively skewed. If the tail is on the left (negative direction), the distribution is negatively skewed.

12-7 Enrichment

Street Networks: Finding All Possible Routes

A section of a city is laid out in square blocks. Going north from the intersection of First Avenue and First Street, the avenues are 1st, 2nd, 3rd, and so on. Going east, the streets are numbered in the same way.

Factorials can be used to find the number, $r(e, n)$, of different routes between two intersections. The formula is shown below.

$$r(e, n) = \frac{[(e - 1) + (n - 1)]!}{(e - 1)!(n - 1)!}$$

The number of streets going east is e; the number of avenues going north is n.

The following problems examine the possible routes from one location to another. Assume that you never use a route that is unnecessarily long. Assume that $e \geq 1$ and $n \geq 1$.

Solve each problem.

1. List all the possible routes from 1st Street and 1st Avenue to 4th Street and 3rd Avenue. Use ordered pairs to show the routes, with street numbers first, and avenue numbers second. For example, each route starts at (1, 1) and ends at (4, 3).

   (1, 1) — (2, 1) — (3, 1) — (4, 1) — (4, 2) — (4, 3)
   (1, 1) — (2, 1) — (3, 1) — (3, 2) — (4, 2) — (4, 3)
   (1, 1) — (2, 1) — (3, 1) — (3, 2) — (3, 3) — (4, 3)
   (1, 1) — (2, 1) — (2, 2) — (3, 2) — (4, 2) — (4, 3)
   (1, 1) — (2, 1) — (2, 2) — (3, 2) — (3, 3) — (4, 3)
   (1, 1) — (2, 1) — (2, 2) — (2, 3) — (3, 3) — (4, 3)
   (1, 1) — (1, 2) — (2, 2) — (3, 2) — (4, 2) — (4, 3)
   (1, 1) — (1, 2) — (2, 2) — (3, 2) — (3, 3) — (4, 3)
   (1, 1) — (1, 2) — (2, 2) — (2, 3) — (3, 3) — (4, 3)
   (1, 1) — (1, 2) — (1, 3) — (2, 3) — (3, 3) — (4, 3)

2. Use the formula to compute the number of routes from (1, 1) to (4, 3). There are 4 streets going east and 3 avenues going north.
   $$\frac{(3 + 2)!}{3!2!} = 10$$

3. Find the number of routes from 1st Street and 1st Avenue to 7th Street and 6th Avenue.
   $$\frac{(6 + 5)!}{6!5!} = 462$$

12-8 Study Guide and Intervention

Binomial Experiments

Binomial Expansions For situations with only 2 possible outcomes, you can use the Binomial Theorem to find probabilities. The coefficients of terms in a binomial expansion can be found by using combinations.

Example **What is the probability that 3 coins show heads and 3 show tails when 6 coins are tossed?**

There are 2 possible outcomes that are equally likely: heads (H) and tails (T). The tosses of 6 coins are independent events. When $(H + T)^6$ is expanded, the term containing H^3T^3, which represents 3 heads and 3 tails, is used to get the desired probability. By the Binomial Theorem the coefficient of H^3T^3 is $C(6, 3)$.

$$P(3 \text{ heads}, 3 \text{ tails}) = \frac{6!}{3!3!}\left(\frac{1}{2}\right)^3\left(\frac{1}{2}\right)^3 \quad P(H)=\frac{1}{2} \text{ and } P(T)=\frac{1}{2}$$
$$= \frac{20}{64}$$
$$= \frac{5}{16}$$

The probability of getting 3 heads and 3 tails is $\frac{5}{16}$ or 0.3125.

Exercises

Find each probability if a coin is tossed 8 times.

1. P(exactly 5 heads)

   about 22%

2. P(exactly 2 heads)

   about 11%

3. P(even number of heads)

   50%

4. P(at least 6 heads)

   about 14%

Mike guesses on all 10 questions of a true-false test. If the answers true and false are evenly distributed, find each probability.

5. Mike gets exactly 8 correct answers. $\frac{45}{1024}$ or 0.044

6. Mike gets at most 3 correct answers. $\frac{11}{64}$ or 0.172

7. A die is tossed 4 times. What is the probability of tossing exactly two sixes? $\frac{25}{216}$ or 0.116

12-8 Study Guide and Intervention (continued)

Binomial Experiments

Binomial Experiments	A binomial experiment is possible if and only if all of these conditions occur. • There are exactly two outcomes for each trial. • There is a fixed number of trials. • The trials are independent. • The probabilities for each trial are the same.

Example **Suppose a coin is weighted so that the probability of getting heads in any one toss is 90%. What is the probability of getting exactly 7 heads in 8 tosses?**

The probability of getting heads is $\frac{9}{10}$, and the probability of getting tails is $\frac{1}{10}$. There are $C(8, 7)$ ways to choose the 7 heads.

$$P(7 \text{ heads}) = C(8, 7)\left(\frac{9}{10}\right)^7\left(\frac{1}{10}\right)^1$$
$$= 8 \cdot \frac{9^7}{10^8}$$
$$\approx 0.38$$

The probability of getting 7 heads in 8 tosses is about 38%.

Exercises

1. **BASKETBALL** For any one foul shot, Derek has a probability of 0.72 of getting the shot in the basket. As part of a practice drill, he shoots 8 shots from the foul line.
   a. What is the probability that he gets in exactly 6 foul shots? about 31%
   b. What is the probability that he gets in at least 6 foul shots? about 60%

2. **SCHOOL** A teacher is trying to decide whether to have 4 or 5 choices per question on her multiple choice test. She wants to prevent students who just guess from scoring well on the test.
   a. On a 5-question multiple-choice test with 4 choices per question, what is the probability that a student can score at least 60% by guessing? 10.4%
   b. What is the probability that a student can score at least 60% by guessing on a test of the same length with 5 choices per question? 5.8%

3. Julie rolls two dice and adds the two numbers.
   a. What is the probability that the sum will be divisible by 3? $\frac{1}{3}$
   b. If she rolls the dice 5 times what is the chance that she will get exactly 3 sums that are divisible by 3? about 16%

4. **SKATING** During practice a skater falls 15% of the time when practicing a triple axel. During one practice session he attempts 20 triple axels.
   a. What is the probability that he will fall only once? about 14%
   b. What is the probability that he will fall 4 times? about 18%

Answers

Lesson 12-8

Skills Practice
Binomial Experiments

Find each probability if a coin is tossed 4 times.

1. P(4 heads) $\frac{1}{16}$
2. P(0 heads) $\frac{1}{16}$
3. P(exactly 3 heads) $\frac{1}{4}$
4. P(exactly 2 heads) $\frac{3}{8}$
5. P(exactly 1 head) $\frac{1}{4}$
6. P(at least 3 heads) $\frac{5}{16}$

Find each probability if a die is rolled 3 times.

7. P(exactly one 2) $\frac{25}{72}$
8. P(exactly two 2s) $\frac{5}{72}$
9. P(exactly three 2s) $\frac{1}{216}$
10. P(at most one 2) $\frac{25}{27}$

A town that presents a fireworks display during its July 4 celebration found the probability that a family with two or more children will watch the fireworks is $\frac{3}{5}$. If 5 of these families are selected at random, find each probability.

11. P(exactly 3 families watch the fireworks) $\frac{216}{625}$
12. P(exactly 2 families watch the fireworks) $\frac{144}{625}$
13. P(exactly 5 families watch the fireworks) $\frac{243}{3125}$
14. P(no families watch the fireworks) $\frac{32}{3125}$
15. P(at least 4 families watch the fireworks) $\frac{1053}{3125}$
16. P(at most 1 family watches the fireworks) $\frac{272}{3125}$

One section of a standardized English language test has 10 true/false questions. Find each probability when a student guesses at all ten questions.

17. P(exactly 8 correct) $\frac{45}{1024}$
18. P(exactly 2 correct) $\frac{45}{1024}$
19. P(exactly half correct) $\frac{63}{256}$
20. P(all 10 correct) $\frac{1}{1024}$
21. P(0 correct) $\frac{1}{1024}$
22. P(at least 8 correct) $\frac{7}{128}$

12-8 Practice (Average)
Binomial Experiments

Find each probability if a coin is tossed 6 times.

1. P(exactly 3 tails) $\frac{5}{16}$
2. P(exactly 5 tails) $\frac{3}{32}$
3. P(0 tails) $\frac{1}{64}$
4. P(at least 4 heads) $\frac{11}{32}$
5. P(at least 4 tails) $\frac{11}{32}$
6. P(at most 2 tails) $\frac{11}{32}$

The probability of Chris making a free throw is $\frac{2}{3}$. If she shoots 5 times, find each probability.

7. P(all missed) $\frac{1}{243}$
8. P(all made) $\frac{32}{243}$
9. P(exactly 2 made) $\frac{40}{243}$
10. P(exactly 1 missed) $\frac{80}{243}$
11. P(at least 3 made) $\frac{64}{81}$
12. P(at most 2 made) $\frac{17}{81}$

When Tarin and Sam play a certain board game, the probability that Tarin will win a game is $\frac{3}{4}$. If they play 5 games, find each probability.

13. P(Sam wins only once) $\frac{405}{1024}$
14. P(Tarin wins exactly twice) $\frac{45}{512}$
15. P(Sam wins exactly 3 games) $\frac{45}{512}$
16. P(Sam wins at least 1 game) $\frac{781}{1024}$
17. P(Tarin wins at least 3 games) $\frac{459}{512}$
18. P(Tarin wins at most 2 games) $\frac{53}{512}$

19. **SAFETY** In August 2001, the American Automobile Association reported that 73% of Americans use seat belts. In a random selection of 10 Americans in 2001, what is the probability that exactly half of them use seat belts? **Source:** AAA **about 7.5%**

HEALTH For Exercises 20 and 21, use the following information.
In 2001, the American Heart Association reported that 50 percent of the Americans who receive heart transplants are ages 50–64 and 20 percent are ages 35–49. **Source:** American Heart Association

20. In a randomly selected group of 10 heart transplant recipients, what is the probability that at least 8 of them are ages 50–64? $\frac{7}{128}$

21. In a randomly selected group of 5 heart transplant recipients, what is the probability that 2 of them are ages 35–49? $\frac{128}{625}$

Lesson 12-8

12-8 Reading to Learn Mathematics

Binomial Experiments

Pre-Activity **How can you determine whether guessing is worth it?**

Read the introduction to Lesson 12-8 at the top of page 676 in your textbook.

Suppose you are taking a 50-question multiple-choice test in which there are 5 answer choices for each question. You are told that no points will be deducted for wrong answers. Should you guess the answers to the questions you do not know? Explain your reasoning. **Sample answer: Yes; the probability of guessing the right answer to a question is $\frac{1}{5}$, so you have a chance to get some points by guessing, and you have nothing to lose.**

Reading the Lesson

1. Indicate whether each of the following is a *binomial experiment or not a binomial experiment*. If the experiment is not a binomial experiment, explain why.

   a. A fair coin is tossed 10 times and "heads" or "tails" is recorded each time. **binomial experiment**

   b. A pair of dice is thrown 5 times and the sum of the numbers that come up is recorded each time. **Not a binomial experiment; there are more than two possible outcomes for each trial.**

   c. There are 5 red marbles and 6 blue marbles in a bag. One marble is drawn from the bag and its color recorded. The marble is not put back in the bag. A second marble is drawn and its color recorded. **Not a binomial experiment; the trials are not independent (or, the probabilities for the two trials are not the same).**

   d. There are 5 red marbles and 6 blue marbles in a bag. One marble is drawn from the bag and its color recorded. The marble is put back in the bag. A second marble is drawn and its color recorded. **binomial experiment**

2. Len randomly guesses the answers to all 6 multiple-choice questions on his chemistry test. Each question has 5 choices. Which of the following expressions gives the probability that he will get at least 4 of the answers correct? **B**

   A. $P(6, 4)\left(\frac{1}{5}\right)^4\left(\frac{4}{5}\right)^2 + P(6, 5)\left(\frac{1}{5}\right)^5\left(\frac{4}{5}\right)^1 + P(6, 6)\left(\frac{1}{5}\right)^6\left(\frac{4}{5}\right)^0$

   B. $C(6, 4)\left(\frac{1}{5}\right)^4\left(\frac{4}{5}\right)^2 + C(6, 5)\left(\frac{1}{5}\right)^5\left(\frac{4}{5}\right)^1 + C(6, 6)\left(\frac{1}{5}\right)^6\left(\frac{4}{5}\right)^0$

   C. $C(6, 4)\left(\frac{1}{5}\right)^2\left(\frac{4}{5}\right)^4 + C(6, 5)\left(\frac{1}{5}\right)^1\left(\frac{4}{5}\right)^5 + C(6, 6)\left(\frac{1}{5}\right)^0\left(\frac{4}{5}\right)^6$

Helping You Remember

3. Some students have trouble remembering how to calculate binomial probabilities. What is an easy way to remember which numbers to put into an expression like $C(6, 4)\left(\frac{1}{5}\right)^2\left(\frac{4}{5}\right)^{14}$? where n is the number of trials and r is the number of successes. The probability of success is raised to the rth power and the probability of failure is raised to the $(n - r)$th power. **Sample answer: The binomial coefficient is $C(n, r)$, where n is the number of trials and r is the number of successes. The probability of success is raised to the rth power and the probability of failure is raised to the $(n - r)$th power.**

12-8 Enrichment

Misuses of Statistics

Statistics can be misleading. Graphs for a set of data can look very different from one another. Compare the following graphs.

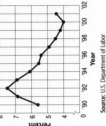

U.S. Unemployment Rate

Source: U.S. Department of Labor

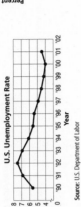

U.S. Unemployment Rate

Source: U.S. Department of Labor

Notice that the two graphs show the same data, but the spacing in the vertical and horizontal scales differs. Scales can be cramped or spread out to make a graph that gives a certain impression. Which graph would you use to give the impression that the unemployment rate dropped dramatically from 1990 to 2000? **the second graph**

Suppose that a car company claims, "75% of people surveyed say that our car is better than the competition." If four people were asked which car they preferred and 75% agreed, how many people thought that *Our Car* was better? **3 people**

The advertisement was misleading in other ways as well. For example, who was surveyed—were the people company employees, or impartial buyers?

Suppose an advertiser claims that 90% of all of one brand of car sold in the last 10 years are still on the road.

1. If 10,000 cars were sold, how many are still on the road? **9,000**

2. If 1000 cars were sold, how many are still on the road? **900**

3. Find an example to show how you think averages could be used in a misleading way. **See students' work.**

4. A survey of a large sample of people who own small computers revealed that 85% of the people thought the instruction manuals should be better written. A manufacturer of small computers claimed that it surveyed many of the same people and found that all of them liked their manuals. Discuss the possible discrepancy in the results. **See students' work.**

Answers

12-9 Study Guide and Intervention

Sampling and Error

Bias A sample of size n is random (or **unbiased**) when every possible sample of size n has an equal chance of being selected. If a sample is biased, then information obtained from it may not be reliable.

Example To find out how people in the U.S. feel about mass transit, people at a commuter train station are asked their opinion. Does this situation represent a random sample?

No; the sample includes only people who actually use a mass-transit facility. The sample does not include people who ride bikes, drive cars, or walk.

Exercises

Determine whether each situation would produce a random sample. Write yes or no and explain your answer.

1. asking people in Phoenix, Arizona, about rainfall to determine the average rainfall for the United States No; it rains less in Phoenix than most places in the U.S.

2. obtaining the names of tree types in North America by surveying all of the U.S. National Forests Yes; there are National Forests in about every state in the U.S.

3. surveying every tenth person who enters the mall to find out about music preferences in that part of the country Yes; mall customers should be fairly representative in terms of music tastes.

4. interviewing country club members to determine the average number of televisions per household in the community No; country club members would tend to be more affluent and thus not a representative sample of the community.

5. surveying all students whose ID numbers end in 4 about their grades and career counseling needs Yes; ID numbers are probably assigned alphabetically or by some other method not connected to students' grades or counseling needs.

6. surveying parents at a day care facility about their preferences for brands of baby food for a marketing campaign Yes; choice of a daycare facility would probably not influence baby food preferences.

7. asking people in a library about the number of magazines to which they subscribe in order to describe the reading habits of a town No; library visitors tend to read more than most citizens.

12-9 Study Guide and Intervention *(continued)*

Sampling and Error

Margin of Error The **margin of sampling error** gives a limit on the difference between how a sample responds and how the total population would respond.

Margin of Error	If the percent of people in a sample responding in a certain way is p and the size of the sample is n, then 95% of the time, the percent of the population responding in that same way will be between $p - ME$ and $p + ME$, where $ME = 2\sqrt{\dfrac{p(1-p)}{n}}$.

Example 1 In a survey of 4500 randomly selected voters, 62% favored candidate A. What is the margin of error?

$ME = 2\sqrt{\dfrac{p(1-p)}{n}}$ Formula for margin of sampling error

$= 2\sqrt{\dfrac{0.62 \cdot (1 - 0.62)}{4500}}$ $p = 62\%$ or 0.62, $n = 4500$

≈ 0.01447 Use a calculator.

The margin of error is about 1%. This means that there is a 95% chance that the percent of voters favoring candidate A is between $62 - 1$ or 61% and $62 + 1$ or 63%.

Example 2 The CD that 32% of teenagers surveyed plan to buy next is the latest from the popular new group BFA. If the margin of error of the survey is 2%, how many teenagers were surveyed?

$ME = 2\sqrt{\dfrac{p(1-p)}{n}}$ Formula for margin of sampling error

$0.02 = 2\sqrt{\dfrac{0.32 \cdot (1 - 0.32)}{n}}$ $ME = 0.02$, $p = 0.32$

$0.01 = \sqrt{\dfrac{0.32(0.68)}{n}}$ Divide each side by 2.

$0.0001 = \dfrac{0.32(0.68)}{n}$ Square each side.

$n = \dfrac{0.32(0.68)}{0.0001}$ Multiply by n and divide by 0.0001.

$n = 2176$

2176 teenagers were surveyed.

Exercises

Find the margin of sampling error to the nearest percent.

1. $p = 45\%$, $n = 350$ about 5%

2. $p = 12\%$, $n = 1500$ about 2%

3. $p = 86\%$, $n = 600$ about 3%

4. A study of 50,000 drivers in Indiana, Illinois, and Ohio showed that 68% preferred a speed limit of 75 mph over 65 mph on highways and country roads. What was the margin of sampling error to the nearest tenth of a percent? about 0.4%

Skills Practice (page 749)

NAME _____ DATE _____ PERIOD _____

12-9 Skills Practice
Sampling and Error

Determine whether each situation would produce a random sample. Write *yes* or *no* and explain your answer.

1. calling households at 3:30 P.M. on Tuesday to determine a political candidate's support No; since most registered voters are likely to be at work at this time, this sample would not be representative of all registered voters.

2. polling customers as they exit a sporting goods store about their attitudes about exercise No; these customers are likely to value exercise more than those who do not shop at sporting goods stores, who are not represented in this survey.

3. recording the number of sit-ups performed by 15-year old girls in the high schools of a large school district to determine the fitness of all high-school girls in the district No; 15-year old girls may not have the same abilities as 18-year old seniors, for example.

4. selecting two of a city's 20 apartment buildings for a survey to determine the desire of apartment dwellers in the city to own a home No; the residents of the two buildings selected might, for example, have nicer apartments or be in a nicer area of town, and thus would not well represent the desires of people in other buildings.

5. In a large school district, the superintendent of schools interviews two teachers at random from each school to determine whether teachers in the district think students are assigned too much or too little homework. Yes; since a cross section of teachers from all levels was selected at random, the sample should well represent the population of teachers in the district.

6. For seven consecutive days, one hour each in the morning, afternoon, and evening, every tenth customer who enters a mall is asked to choose her or his favorite store. Yes; because the sample is chosen over the course of a whole week, during hours when different consumer groups shop, and because the selection is systematic, the sample should well represent the general population that shops at the mall stores.

Find the margin of sampling error to the nearest percent.

7. $p = 85\%, n = 100$ about 7%

8. $p = 78\%, n = 100$ about 8%

9. $p = 15\%, n = 100$ about 7%

10. $p = 37\%, n = 500$ about 4%

11. $p = 12\%, n = 500$ about 3%

12. $p = 93\%, n = 500$ about 2%

13. $p = 23\%, n = 1000$ about 3%

14. $p = 56\%, n = 1000$ about 3%

15. **HEALTH** In a recent poll of cigarette smokers, 67% of those surveyed said they had tried to quit smoking within the last year. The margin of error was 3%. About how many people were surveyed? about 983

Practice (page 750)

NAME _____ DATE _____ PERIOD _____

12-9 Practice (Average)
Sampling and Error

Determine whether each situation would produce a random sample. Write *yes* or *no* and explain your answer.

1. calling every twentieth registered voter to determine whether people own or rent their homes in your community No; registered voters may be more likely to be homeowners, causing the survey to underrepresent renters.

2. predicting local election results by polling people in every twentieth residence in all the different neighborhoods of your community Yes; since all neighborhoods are represented proportionally, the views of the community should as a whole should be well represented.

3. to find out why not many students are using the library, a school's librarian gives a questionnaire to every tenth student entering the library No; she is polling only the students who are coming to the library, and will obtain no input from those who aren't using the library.

4. testing overall performance of tires on interstate highways only No; for overall performance, tires should be tested on many kinds of surfaces, and under many types of conditions.

5. selecting every 50th hamburger from a fast-food restaurant chain and determining its fat content to assess the fat content of hamburgers served in fast-food restaurant chains throughout the country No; the selected hamburgers are a random sample of the hamburgers served in one chain, and may represent the fat content for that chain, but will not necessarily represent the fat content of hamburgers served in other fast-food restaurant chains.

6. assigning all shift workers in a manufacturing plant a unique identification number, and then placing the numbers in a hat and drawing 30 at random to determine the annual average salary of the workers Yes; because the numbers are randomly chosen from among all shift workers, all workers have the same chance of being selected.

Find the margin of sampling error to the nearest percent.

7. $p = 26\%, n = 100$ about 9%

8. $p = 55\%, n = 100$ about 10%

9. $p = 75\%, n = 500$ about 4%

10. $p = 14\%, n = 500$ about 3%

11. $p = 96\%, n = 1000$ about 1%

12. $p = 21\%, n = 1000$ about 3%

13. $p = 34\%, n = 1000$ about 3%

14. $p = 49\%, n = 1500$ about 3%

15. $p = 65\%, n = 1500$ about 2%

16. **COMPUTING** According to a poll of 500 teenagers, 43% said that they use a personal computer at home. What is the margin of sampling error? about 4%

17. **TRUST** A survey of 605 people, ages 13–33, shows that 68% trust their parents more than their best friends to tell them the truth. What is the margin of sampling error? about 4%

18. **PRODUCTIVITY** A study by the University of Illinois in 1995 showed an increase in productivity by 10% of the employees who wore headsets and listened to music of their choice while they were working. The margin of sampling error for the study was about 7%. How many employees participated in the study? about 73

12-9 Enrichment

Shapes of Distribution Curves

Graphs of frequency distributions can be described as either symmetric or skewed.

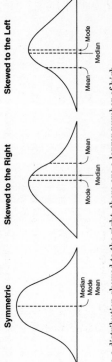

Symmetric   Skewed to the Right   Skewed to the Left

In a distribution skewed to the right, there are a larger number of high values. The long "tail" extends to the right.

In a distribution skewed to the left, there are a larger number of low values. The "tail" extends to the left.

For each of the following, state whether the distribution is symmetric or skewed. If it is skewed, tell whether it is skewed to the right or to the left.

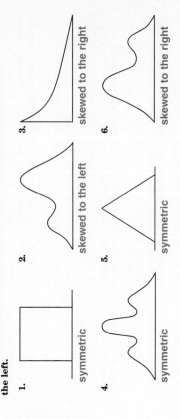

1. symmetric

2. skewed to the left

3. skewed to the right

4. symmetric

5. skewed to the left

6. skewed to the right

A vertical line above the median divides the area under a frequency curve in half.

7. Where is the median in a symmetric distribution? In the middle of the range; it is the same as the mean.

8. Where is the median in a skewed distribution? To the left of the middle if skewed to the right; to the right of the middle if skewed to the left.

Lesson 12-9

12-9 Reading to Learn Mathematics

Sampling and Error

Pre-Activity **How are opinion polls used in political campaigns?**

Read the introduction to Lesson 12-9 at the top of page 682 in your textbook.

Do you think the results of the survey about the presidential preferences demonstrates that Bush was actually ahead in Florida a month before the election? If there is not enough information given to determine this, list at least two questions you would ask about the survey that would help you determine the significance of the survey. Sample answer: There is not enough information to tell. 1. How many people were surveyed? 2. How was the sample for the survey selected? 3. What is the margin of error for this survey?

Reading the Lesson

1. Determine whether each situation would produce a random sample. Write *yes* or *no* and explain your answer.

a. asking all the customers at five restaurants on the same evening how many times a month they eat dinner in restaurants to determine how often the average American eats dinner in a restaurant. No; people surveyed at a restaurant might be likely to eat dinner in restaurants more often than other people.

b. putting the names of all seniors at your high school in a hat and then drawing 20 names for a survey to find out where seniors would like to hold their prom. Yes; every senior would have an equal chance of being chosen for the survey.

2. A survey determined that 58% of registered voters in the United States support increased federal spending for education. The margin of error for this survey is 4%. Explain in your own words what this tells you about the actual percentage of registered voters who support increased spending for education. Sample answer: There is a 95% chance that the actual percentage of voters supporting increased federal spending for education is between 54% and 62%.

Helping You Remember

3. The formula for margin of sampling error may be tricky to remember. A good way to start is to think about the variables that must be included in the formula. What are these variables, and what do they represent? What is an easy way to remember which variable goes in the denominator in the formula? Sample answer: *p* is the probability of a certain response and *n* is the sample size. The larger the sample size, the smaller the margin of error, so *n* must go in the denominator since dividing by a larger number gives a smaller number. The square root of a smaller number is a smaller number, and twice the square root of a smaller number is a smaller number.

Chapter 12 Assessment Answer Key

1. __A__

2. __D__

3. __C__

4. __B__

5. __D__

6. __A__

7. __B__

8. __C__

9. __A__

10. __D__

11. __D__

12. __C__

13. __B__

14. __A__

15. __C__

16. __A__

17. __C__

18. __B__

19. __C__

20. __B__

B: __$4f^3n; \dfrac{5}{324}$__

1. __B__

2. __D__

3. __A__

4. __A__

5. __B__

6. __A__

7. __C__

8. __B__

9. __B__

10. __C__

11. __B__

(continued on the next page)

Answers

Chapter 12 Assessment Answer Key

Form 2A *(continued)*
Page 756

12. __C__

13. __B__

14. __A__

15. __B__

16. __A__

17. __D__

18. __C__

19. __C__

20. __A__

B: __{7, 10, 17, 24, 26, 28, 28}__
Sample answer:

Form 2B
Page 757

1. __C__

2. __A__

3. __D__

4. __B__

5. __D__

6. __C__

7. __C__

8. __B__

9. __A__

10. __D__

11. __D__

Page 758

12. __A__

13. __C__

14. __D__

15. __B__

16. __A__

17. __A__

18. __C__

19. __C__

20. __A__

B: __{7, 9, 18, 20, 24, 40, 50}__
Sample answer:

Glencoe Algebra 2

Chapter 12 Assessment Answer Key

Form 2C
Page 759

1. _____72_____

2. _____120_____

3. _____1320_____

4. _____3003_____

5. $\dfrac{4}{11}$

6. $\dfrac{5}{12}$

7. $\dfrac{125}{216}$

8. $\dfrac{4}{663}$

9. $\dfrac{19}{91}$

10. $\dfrac{2}{5}$

11. $\dfrac{1}{16}$

12. $\dfrac{147}{512}$

13. _____3360_____

Page 760

14. __Mode; it is the lowest.__

15. _____106.0°F_____

16. _____10.3°F_____

17. __normally distributed__

18. _____47.5%_____

19. No, the opinions of one class may not be typical of all members of their age group.

20. _____about 9%_____

B: _____74; 4_____

Answers

Chapter 12 Assessment Answer Key

Form 2D
Page 761

1. _____105_____

2. _____24_____

3. _____60_____

4. _____792_____

5. _____5:7_____

6. _____$\dfrac{4}{7}$_____

7. _____$\dfrac{1}{216}$_____

8. _____$\dfrac{1}{221}$_____

9. _____$\dfrac{8}{99}$_____

10. _____$\dfrac{9}{20}$_____

11. _____$\dfrac{9}{256}$_____

12. _____$\dfrac{54}{125}$_____

Page 762

13. _____630_____

14. **Sample answer: Median; it is closer to most of the values.**

15. _____0.02_____

16. _____0.15 in._____

17. **positively skewed**

18. _____47.5%_____

19. **No, library card holders may not have opinions that are typical of the community.**

20. _____about 13%_____

B: _____77; 3_____

Chapter 12 Assessment Answer Key

Form 3

Page 763

Page 764

1. _____7776_____

2. _____80,640_____

3. _70; combination; order does not matter._

4. _____162,162_____

5. $\dfrac{4}{17}$

6. $\dfrac{1}{2}$

7. $\dfrac{1}{216}$

8. $\dfrac{169}{41,650}$

9. $\dfrac{13}{34}$

10. $\dfrac{55}{221}$

11. _____34,560_____

12. **Sample answer: Mean; the Maryland taxes are above the median but they are below the mean.**

13. ____126,875.81____

14. _____$356.20_____

15. **positively skewed**

16. _____4890_____

17. $\dfrac{203}{23,328}$

18. _____0.05_____

19. **No, drivers may not have the same opinion as nondrivers in the town.**

20. **about 348 people**

B: **about 1275 students**

Answers

Chapter 12 Assessment Answer Key

Page 765, Open-Ended Assessment
Scoring Rubric

Score	General Description	Specific Criteria
4	**Superior** A correct solution that is supported by well-developed, accurate explanations	• Shows thorough understanding of the concepts of *solving problems involving finding probability, independent and dependent events, permutations, combinations, mutually exclusive and inclusive events, statistical measures,* and *the normal distribution* • Uses appropriate strategies to solve problems. • Computations are correct. • Written explanations are exemplary. • Goes beyond requirements of some or all problems.
3	**Satisfactory** A generally correct solution, but may contain minor flaws in reasoning or computation	• Shows an understanding of the concepts of *solving problems involving finding probability, independent and dependent events, permutations, combinations, mutually exclusive and inclusive events, statistical measures,* and *the normal distribution* • Uses appropriate strategies to solve problems. • Computations are mostly correct. • Written explanations are effective. • Satisfies all requirements of problems.
2	**Nearly Satisfactory** A partially correct interpretation and/or solution to the problem	• Shows an understanding of most of the concepts of *solving problems involving finding probability, independent and dependent events, permutations, combinations, mutually exclusive and inclusive events, statistical measures,* and *the normal distribution* • May not use appropriate strategies to solve problems. • Computations are mostly correct. • Written explanations are satisfactory. • Satisfies the requirements of most of the problems.
1	**Nearly Unsatisfactory** A correct solution with no supporting evidence or explanation	• Final computation is correct. • No written explanations or work is shown to substantiate the final computation. • Satisfies minimal requirements of some of the problems.
0	**Unsatisfactory** An incorrect solution indicating no mathematical understanding of the concept or task, or no solution is given	• Shows little or no understanding of most of the concepts of *solving problems involving finding probability, independent and dependent events, permutations, combinations, mutually exclusive and inclusive events, statistical measures,* and *the normal distribution* • Does not use appropriate strategies to solve problems. • Computations are incorrect. • Written explanations are unsatisfactory. • Does not satisfy the requirements of problems. • No answer may be given.

Chapter 12 Assessment Answer Key

In addition to the scoring rubric found on page A34, the following sample answers may be used as guidance in evaluating open-ended assessment items.

1a. Student responses must indicate that Alma's solution is correct. Explanations should indicate that, since A and B represent two independent events and they are looking for the probability that both events occurred, the two probabilities should be multiplied. Addition would be required if they were looking for the probability of either one of the events to occur.

1b. Sample answer for Steven's solution $P(A) + P(B) - P(A \text{ and } B) =$ $\frac{2}{6} + \frac{3}{6} - \frac{1}{6} = \frac{4}{6} = \frac{2}{3}$: A die is rolled. Find the probability that a number greater than 4 or an even number is rolled.

2a. The student response should indicate that for grades listed, left to right, from lowest to highest, a negatively skewed distribution would include a greater number of high scores than low scores. Thus, the student should be happy!

2b. Students should explain that the mean, median, and mode of a normal distribution are the same, so the mean can be presumed to be $\frac{56 + 98}{2} = 77$, or very close to 77. The fact that there are three standard deviations between 77 and 98 (or between 56 and 77) means that the standard deviation is $\frac{98 - 77}{3} = 7$ $\left(\text{or } \frac{77 - 56}{3} = 7\right)$. Thus, scores in the range 77 ± 7, or between 70 and 84, would earn a grade of C.

3a. Sample answer: For 6 dinner guests, there would be 8 players including Greg and Jacqui, meaning that there would be 70 different ways to arrange the guests in two teams; students should indicate that this is a problem involving combinations, rather than permutations since changing the order in which players are selected for each team would not result in the formation of different teams.

3b. Students should state that this new condition would, in fact, change the number of arrangements. Taking Greg and Jacqui out of the situation for the moment, the question, for the sample answer in part **a**, would become: In how many ways can you divide a group of 6 people into two groups of 3 people each? The number of ways to do so would be $C(6, 3) = 20$. Then, since there are two ways to place Greg with one group and Jacqui with the other, there are only $20 \cdot 2 = 40$ possible arrangements if Greg and Jacqui cannot be on the same team.

Answers

Chapter 12 Assessment Answer Key

Vocabulary Test/Review
Page 766

1. false; combination

2. true

3. false; standard deviation

4. false; discrete probability distributions

5. false; binomial experiment

6. true

7. true

8. false; compound events

9. false; measures of central tendency

10. false; skewed distribution

11. Sample answer: Mutually exclusive events are events that cannot both happen at the same time.

12. A sample is a random sample every possible sample of that size has an equal chance of being chosen.

Quiz (Lessons 12–1 through 12–3)
Page 767

1. _____ D _____

2. _____ 5040 _____

3. combination; 175

4. $\frac{9}{20}$; 9:11

5. $\frac{2}{7}$

Quiz (Lessons 12–4 and 12–5)
Page 767

1. $\frac{4}{9}$

2. $\frac{16}{675}$

3. $\frac{8}{273}$

4. $\frac{1}{4}$

5. $\frac{11}{26}$

Quiz (Lessons 12–6 and 12–7)
Page 768

1. _____ 4.69 _____

2. _____ 2.17 _____

3. positively skewed

4. _____ 68% _____

5. _____ 396 _____

Quiz (Lessons 12–8 and 12–9)
Page 768

1. $\frac{5}{72}$

2. $\frac{215}{216}$

3. $\frac{11}{243}$

4. No, the people surveyed are more likely to prefer basketball over other sports.

5. _____ about 11% _____

Chapter 12 Assessment Answer Key

Mid-Chapter Test
Page 769

1. **C**

2. **B**

3. **D**

4. **D**

5. **A**

6. **C**

7. $\dfrac{56}{969}$

8. $\dfrac{49}{99}$

9. $\dfrac{4}{5}$

10. **24**

11. $\dfrac{1}{2}$

12. **1140**

Cumulative Review
Page 770

1. $R'(-3, -1),$
   $S'(4, 2),\ T'(3, -4)$

2. $-3x^2 + 5x + 12$

3. **no**

4.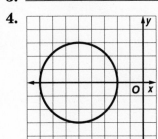

5.
$f(x) = -\dfrac{2}{(x-1)^2}$

6. $w < -1$

7. $1000^{-1/3} = \dfrac{1}{10}$

8. **7.3 yr**

9. $2, -1, -4$

10. $9, 3, 1, \dfrac{1}{3}$

11. $\dfrac{209}{333}$

12. **19,958,400**

13. $\dfrac{2}{5525}$

14. **47.5%**

15. **about 6%**

Answers

Chapter 12 Assessment Answer Key

Standardized Test Practice

Page 771

1. Ⓐ Ⓑ Ⓒ ●D

2. Ⓔ Ⓕ ●G Ⓗ

3. ●A Ⓑ Ⓒ Ⓓ

4. Ⓔ ●F Ⓖ Ⓗ

5. ●A Ⓑ Ⓒ Ⓓ

6. Ⓔ Ⓕ ●G Ⓗ

7. ●A Ⓑ Ⓒ Ⓓ

8. Ⓔ Ⓕ Ⓖ ●H

9. Ⓐ Ⓑ Ⓒ ●D

10. Ⓔ ●F Ⓖ Ⓗ

Page 772

11. 1 6

12. 2 4 3

13. 3 1 . 5

14. 7 0

15. ●A Ⓑ Ⓒ Ⓓ

16. Ⓐ Ⓑ Ⓒ ●D

17. Ⓐ Ⓑ ●C Ⓓ

Chapter 12 Assessment Answer Key

Unit 4 Test
Page 773

1. __22, 28, 34, 40__

2. __19, 17, 15__

3. __7__

4. __3200, 2560__

5. __3072, 2304, 1728, 1296__

6. __63__

7. __96__

8. __108__

9. __$\dfrac{245}{333}$__

10. __5, 16, 49, 148, 445__

11. __1, −3, −11__

12. __$810xy^4$__

13. __See students' answers.__

14. __Sample answer: $n = 2$__

15. __240__

16. __5040__

Page 774

17. __66__

18. __8:5__

19. __$\dfrac{1}{6}$__

20. __$\dfrac{1}{3}$__

21. __$\dfrac{7}{13}$__

22. __374.88; 356; no mode; 243.67__

23. __positively skewed__

24. __0.5%__

25. __$\dfrac{45}{512}$__

26. __Sample answer: No; those surveyed are more likely to listen to a station that airs the type of music being performed at the concert.__

Glencoe Algebra 2

Answers